Astronomy and the Origin of the Earth

Astronomy and the Origin of the Earth

BROWN FOUNDATIONS OF EARTH SCIENCE SERIES

Theodore G. Mehlin
Williams College

WM. C. BROWN COMPANY PUBLISHERS
Dubuque, Iowa

Man is a creature of the earth. Second to knowledge of man himself is the necessity to understand the earth. The comprehensive study of the earth and its phenomena is termed earth science. The subject area intersects numerous college disciplines. To gain a thorough scientific understanding of the earth, one must study astronomy, meteorology, oceanography, geology and geophysics, plus aspects of geography and engineering. Additionally, comprehension of these topics requires a prior knowledge of such areas as mathematics, physics, chemistry and biology.

The knowledge explosion which has occurred during the twentieth century has made this approach impossible for the educated layman. Nevertheless, the need to understand our earth has become increasingly necessary.

The **FOUNDATIONS OF EARTH SCIENCE** Series, designed for use at the introductory level, incorporates into the scientific study of the earth an understanding of what components comprise the earth, their distribution, and an understanding of how and why they exist as they are, and how they affect civilized man.

The study of the origin of the earth is a problem in astronomy. In order to understand the theories used to explain the origin of the earth, some basic elements of astronomy must be understood. Through the utilization of the science of astronomy, **Astronomy and the Origin of the Earth** offers explanations for the beginning of the earth and its early history.

Biology

FOSSILS, PALEONTOLOGY
AND EVOLUTION

David L. Clark
University of Wisconsin

History

HISTORICAL GEOLOGY OF
NORTH AMERICA

R. L. Langenheim, Jr.
University of Illinois

STRATIGRAPHY AND
GEOLOGIC TIME

John W. Harbaugh
Stanford University

Geography
Oceanography   Geodesy   Climatology
Cartography

GEOGRAPHY,
CLIMATOLOGY
AND OCEANOGRAPHY

George R. Rumney
University of Connecticut

BROWN
FOUNDATIONS
OF
EARTH
SCIENCE
SERIES

**Quaternary Studies and
Archeology**

PLEISTOCENE GLACIATION
AND THE COMING OF MAN

W. N. Melhorn
Purdue University

**Physical Geography and
Hydrology**

LANDFORMS AND
LANDSCAPES

Sherwood D. Tuttle
University of Iowa

Chemistry

EARTH MATERIALS

Henry Wenden
Ohio State University

Engineering and Mining

APPLIED EARTH SCIENCE

Daniel S. Turner
Eastern Michigan University

Physics

STRUCTURES, TECTONICS
AND GEOPHYSICS

John S. Sumner
University of Arizona

Astronomy

ASTRONOMY AND THE
ORIGIN OF THE EARTH

Theodore G. Mehlin
Williams College

Preface

Long before history was recorded, early man must have noticed the rising and the setting of the sun, the changing phases of the moon and the richly star-studded sky of a clear night. If this can be called astronomy, then astronomy can perhaps claim to be the oldest of the sciences.

In the Greek period, twenty centuries ago, scientific observations were made and philosophical hypotheses were proposed in an attempt to explain the organization of the universe as it was then understood. With the invention of telescopes early in the seventeenth century, new impetus was given to observation, and our knowledge of astronomy has grown at an ever-increasing rate down through the years. During the last four decades, the completion of large visual telescopes, the whole new field of radio astronomy and the development of artificial satellites and space probes have contributed to an almost explosive increase in our understanding of the universe in which we live. In spite of this, that which remains to be discovered must be vastly greater than that which we know.

It must be obvious that a book the size of this one can present only a small fraction of our present knowledge of astronomy. If it can bring to its readers a basic understanding of the sun, the moon, the planets, the stars and the galaxies it will have fulfilled its purpose.

Contents

What Is Astronomy?

Astronomy is the science which is trying to achieve the greatest possible understanding of the nature of the universe. In a field so vast there are, of course, a great many old questions which are as yet unanswered, and new questions appear every day. The careful student of astronomy cannot fail to be impressed both by the tremendous bulk of knowledge that has already accumulated and by the high degree of precision with which many of the questions of past generations have been answered.

The origin of the earth cannot be divorced from the origin of the other planets in the solar system or from the origin of the sun itself. Since our sun is a typical star, one of a hundred billion which make up the Milky Way Galaxy, we become involved in stellar evolution. Our Milky Way Galaxy, however, is merely one of at least ten billion comparable systems within the reach of our present telescopes. Thus, any comprehensive study of the origin of the earth must include a consideration of the age and origin of the entire universe.

Before we proceed to a more detailed consideration of the various aspects of the astronomical universe, it may be helpful to orient ourselves with a rapid survey.

Our sun is a typical star and, as far as we can tell, is differentiated from millions of other stars having similar characteristics only because of its relative proximity to us. The sun is entirely gaseous, composed largely of hydrogen. In the central regions of the sun both the temperature and the pressure are so extremly high that energy-producing nuclear reactions are going on constantly. The outward flow of energy maintains the photosphere, or visible surface of the sun at a temperature of 6000°K (11,000°F). The energy radiated by the photosphere constitutes the only significant source of heat and light for all the planets in the solar system.

The sun has a family of nine planets, of which the earth is the third outward from the sun. All the planets move in more or less circular orbits around the sun, and all are in relatively the same plane. They range in size from Mercury, only 3000 miles in diameter, to Jupiter, 86,000 miles in diameter, eleven times the diameter of the earth. Mercury, the innermost planet, is only 0.4 of the earth's distance from the sun and receives solar radiation more than six times as intense as the radiation we receive on the earth. Pluto, the outermost known planet, is 39.5 times the earth's distance from the sun, and the sunlight it receives is only 1/16 of one per cent as strong as ours. Temperatures on the various planets lie between a high of 770°F for Mercury and a low of −350°F for Pluto.

Six of the nine planets have from one to a dozen satellites. Two of Jupiter's are as large as Mercury, and two are about the size of our moon, 2000 miles in diameter. Some of the smaller satellites may be only five to ten miles in their longest dimension, comparable to a single, rather large mountain.

Many thousand asteroids are located primarily between the orbits of Mars and Jupiter, that is, between 1.5 and 5.2 times the earth's distance from the sun. These are solid bodies, the largest 480 miles in diameter, but most of them only a few miles, or a few tens of miles in size. Several thousand have been identified, but there are certainly many thousands more that have not been carefully observed.

The earth, speeding along 18.5 miles per second in its orbit around the sun, runs into more than twenty-five million tiny particles of matter each day. When they hit our air the friction heats them to incandescence and we see them as the tiny points of light flashing across the sky which we call shooting stars or, more properly, meteors.

Each year several new comets are seen. They are members of the solar system and seem to originate far beyond the outermost known planet, moving in toward the sun and picking up speed as the sun's gravitational pull becomes stronger with the decreasing distance. Many comets develop a tail made of material evaporated from the nucleus by the solar radiation and forced back away from the sun by the strength of this same radiation.

It thus becomes apparent that the sun has gravitational control over a wide variety of objects. Since our sun seems to be a perfectly typical star, one may reasonably ask whether other stars have similar systems about them. From a probability standpoint it would seem almost certain that our solar system is not unique. It can be demonstrated that if the very nearest star had a planetary system identical to our sun's, not a single member of that family would be detectable in our most powerful telescope. Thus, the fact that no planets have been observed directly around stars is no proof of their nonexistence. Most astronomers feel that many, though probably not all, of the stars may have planetary systems associated with them.

Our sun has been mentioned as a typical star. In the entire sky there are only about six thousand stars bright enough to be seen with the naked eye, but our largest telescopes can photograph about ten billion. Most of them are intrinsically fainter than our sun, some only 1/10,000 as bright. Among those brighter than the sun, a few have ten thousand times the sun's luminosity. Some of them are not much larger than the largest planets; others are so huge that they could contain not only the sun, but the orbits of Mercury, Venus, Earth and Mars. Yet all are similar to the sun in that they are great balls of gas which in their interiors produce energy by nuclear reactions and radiate this energy in the form of light from their photospheres.

As we look at the night sky we find that almost all the stars visible in even our largest telescopes are members of our own Milky Way Galaxy. This is a tremendous, flat, spiral structure between 80,000 and 100,000 light years in diameter (a light year is about 6 million million miles) and 8 to 10,000 light years thick at the center. It contains approximately one hundred billion stars. From an almost spherical central nucleus two spiral arms wind outward, like a gigantic pinwheel. Within the arms are vast clouds of gas and dust, the galactic nebulae, which may contain up to 20 per cent of the mass of the arms. Surrounding this flattened system is a nearly spherical volume, more sparsely populated with stars, but including in its outer regions over a hundred globular star clusters which contain from a few thousand to a few hundred thousand stars each. The entire Milky Way Galaxy is rotating, the central regions more rapidly than the outlying portions, so that the spiral arms are becoming more tightly wound around the nucleus.

If our own Galaxy does not provide enough material to keep the astronomers busy, there are at least ten billion other galaxies, more or less similar to our own, within the reach of our present telescopes. Their distribution is quite irregular, but the average distance between adjacent galaxies is probably about 2 million light years. The most distant systems that have been observed are 6 to 8 billion light years from the sun, but this should not be interpreted as representing the size of the universe. Rather, it simply represents the limit of our present telescopic power.

This is the scope of astronomy. We will here try to give the astronomer's picture of the universe as it is today, together with the most generally accepted theories of how it reached its present state of development.

2

Telescopes and Light

TOPICS

Visual telescopes

Photographic telescopes

Catadioptric telescopes

Radio telescopes

Atomic structure

Spectroscopy

Measurement of radial velocity

Except for what we know about the earth itself and about meteorites that have fallen onto the earth, all the information which astronomers have used to put together the modern picture of the universe has reached us as radiation, in the form of either light or radio waves. When our first landing party reaches the moon, this statement will need to be altered slightly, but with the exception of the moon and perhaps some of the nearer planets, the statement will stand for a long time. Thus, it seems appropriate to consider the instruments which are used in astronomical investigations and the nature of the radiation which is observed.

OPTICAL TELESCOPES

Telescopic astronomy began in 1609 when Galileo of Padua, Italy, made his first telescope and used it for astronomical observations.

The heart of any telescope is its objective, which may be one or more lenses, one or more mirrors or a combination of mirrors and lenses. Its purpose is to form as bright and as clear an image of a section of the sky as is possible. This image may then be studied visually with an eye-piece or ocular, it may be photographed by placing a photographic plate in the plane of the image, the brightness of the image may be measured

4

by a suitable photometer, or the physical characteristics of the light may be analyzed with a spectrograph.

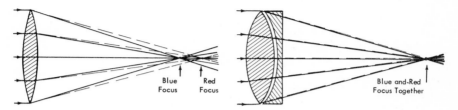

Figure 2.1. The simple lens, left, has a different focal point for each color. The achromatic objective, right, brings a wide range of colors to almost the same focal point.

The objective of early refracting telescopes was a single converging lens, but the different colors of light were not focused at the same point and various other aberrations caused the image to be somewhat blurred. About 1759 John Dollond produced an achromatic objective by combining a converging lens of crown glass with a diverging lens of flint glass. The color correction was quite satisfactory, and with four lens surfaces to work with, the lens designer could minimize the other aberrations. The largest refracting telescope in the world, completed in 1895, is at the Yerkes Observatory at Williams Bay, Wisconsin. Its objective is 40 inches in diameter and has a focal length of 64 feet.

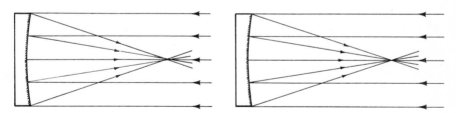

Figure 2.2. The spherical mirror left, produces no sharp focus. The parabolic mirror, right, focuses incoming parallel rays at a single point.

Sir Isaac Newton made the first reflecting telescope in 1672. By using a concave mirror to reflect the light to a focus, all chromatic aberration is eliminated, and by making the mirror parabolic in cross section all incoming rays of light which are parallel to the axis of the mirror are brought to exactly the same focus. Modern reflecting telescopes have a thick Pyrex or quartz mirror whose top surface is within a few millionths of an inch of the theoretical curve. A thin reflecting coat of pure aluminum is evaporated onto this front surface so that the light does not pass through the Pyrex or quartz at all. The largest reflecting telescope is the Hale Telescope at the Palomar Observatory. Its mirror is 200 inches in diameter and its focal length is 55 feet.

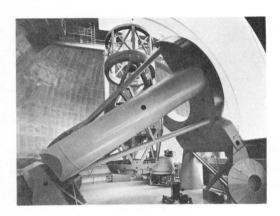

Figure 2.3. The 200-inch Hale Telescope on Palomar Mountain is the world's largest optical telescope. Photograph from the Mount Wilson and Palomar Observatories.

With parabolic reflectors the image quality deteriorates rapidly at even small distances from the center of the field. To permit precise photographs of larger areas of the sky a whole family of catadioptric telescopes has been developed during the last few decades. They combine one or two mirrors with a thin lens which frequently has nonspherical surfaces, and produce critically sharp images over a field that may be as much as 25 degrees in diameter. The most widely used instruments of this class are the Schmidt telescopes.

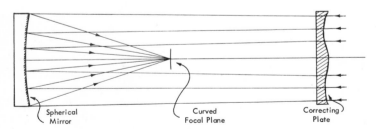

Spherical Mirror   Curved Focal Plane   Correcting Plate

Figure 2.4. The Schmidt telescope combines a thin correcting plate and a spherical mirror to produce excellent images over a wide area of the sky.

RADIO TELESCOPES

The electromagnetic spectrum encompasses a very wide range of frequencies, from wavelengths shorter than a billionth of an inch to waves over 15 miles long. It thus has a length of over fifty octaves. Our eyes are sensitive only to waves between 1/60,000 and 1/30,000 inch, or about one octave. With special instruments we can photograph a total range of about four octaves, but outside of this our atmosphere was once believed to be opaque to incoming radiation.

In 1931 Karl G. Jansky of the Bell Telephone Laboratory observed radio waves that originated in the Milky Way. When Jansky and his followers found that there was a "radio window" in our atmosphere through which radio waves from 1/10 inch to 25 feet in length could reach us from outer space they opened a whole new field of investigation, radio astronomy. In 1951 E. M. Purcell and H. I. Ewen first observed the 21-centimeter (8-inch) hydrogen radiation which had been predicted theoretically. This has been particularly valuable because great clouds of hydrogen occupy large portions of our galaxy.

Radio telescopes look very different from visual telescopes. Many have a large parabolic "dish" covered with metal plates or screening which reflects the radio waves to a focus on the antenna of a tuned radio receiver. The strength of the incoming radio signal is measured at many points in an area of the sky, and a chart can then be made showing the relative radio activity.

The considerable length of the radio waves compared to visual light is an advantage in that they penetrate the vast clouds of dust which

Figure 2.5. The 250-foot Jodrell Bank Radio Telescope of the University of Manchester, England, is the world's largest "steerable dish." A 50-foot radio telescope for tracking satellites and space probes is in the foreground. British Crown Copyright.

occur in the galaxy and limit our optical view. This longer wavelength, however, causes radio telescopes to be very much less precise in pinpointing positions or sizes of objects than are optical telescopes.

ATOMIC STRUCTURE

All of the ninety-two kinds of natural atoms are made up of only three types of basic particles: protons, neutrons and electrons. The atomic physicist recognizes several small secondary particles in addition, but they need not concern us. Protons and neutrons are about equally massive; protons have a unit positive charge, and neutrons are electrically neutral. An electron has a unit negative charge and its mass is 1/1840 that of a proton.

An hydrogen nucleus is a single proton. The nuclei of all other atoms are made up of a number of protons with, usually, an equal or greater number of neutrons. The number of protons determines the element. For example, any atom having two protons in the nucleus is helium; lithium has three protons; iron has twenty-six and uranium ninety-two. In some cases, there is a variation in the number of neutrons found in the nucleus, and these different forms of the same element are called isotopes. Uranium normally has one hundred forty-six neutrons in each nucleus. A lighter isotope having only one hundred forty-three electrons is the unstable form used in the uranium bomb.

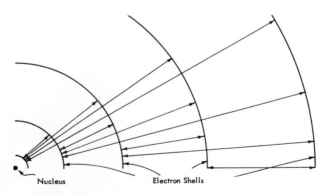

Nucleus   Electron Shells

Figure 2.6. Possible electron jumps between the inner five energy levels within an atom.

Each neutral atom has the same number of negative electrons that it has positive protons. The electrons are positioned in a set of specific shells for each kind of atom, and usually occupy the smallest possible shells. When an atom absorbs energy an electron is lifted from a smaller shell to a larger one, and the atom is said to be excited. Usually within less than a millionth of a second the electron drops back to its lower energy level, giving off a quantum of light having exactly the same energy as that which the atom had previously absorbed. The greater the amount of energy in the quantum, the higher the frequency and the bluer the light given off. Since all the individual atoms of a particular element have identical energy levels, they will all give off the same pattern of colors. Different elements, however, have different sets of electron shells, so the pattern of colors given off differs from one element to another. This provides a means of establishing what elements are involved in the absorption or emission of light.

SPECTROSCOPY

A spectrograph is an instrument used to analyze light. The light is admitted through a narrow slit, rendered parallel by a lens, deflected by a prism or grating and then focused by another lens onto the photographic plate. The amount of the deflection depends on the wavelength or color of the light. The spectrum is thus a series of monochromatic images of the slit, with the long-wave red images at one end and the short-wave blue images at the other.

If the radiating source is a gas under low pressure only specific colors will be present and the spectrum will consist of a series of bright lines against a dark background. If the source is a gas under high pressure, a liquid or a solid, the spectrum will be a continuous band of color from red to blue. If the light from a source giving off a continuous

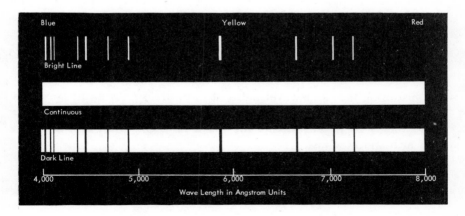

Figure 2.7. Kirchoff's three basic types of spectra.

spectrum passes through a gas under low pressure, the gas will absorb only those colors which it is capable of emitting and the result will be a series of dark lines superimposed on the continuous spectrum. Thus, in most astronomical situations we can tell both the physical nature of the source and its chemical composition.

Measurement of Radial Velocity

If the source of light and the observer are approaching each other the waves will be slightly crowded together, resulting in shorter wavelengths, higher frequency and a shift toward the blue end of the spectrum. If the source and the observer are receding from each other, the waves will be slightly lengthened, the frequency lowered and the position of the lines in the spectrum will be shifted slightly toward the red. This

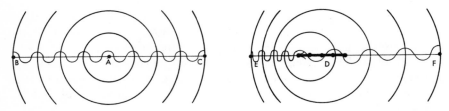

Figure 2.8. With a stationary source at A, observers at B and C will observe light waves of normal length. With a moving source, D, an observer at E will see the waves shorter than normal, and an observer at F will see them elongated.

is called the Doppler effect. The amount of the shift is proportional to the relative speeds:

$$\frac{\text{change of wavelength}}{\text{normal wavelength}} = \frac{\text{speed of approach or recession}}{\text{velocity of light}}$$

By measuring the exact wavelengths of the various lines in the spectrum of a star and comparing them with the normal wave lengths for those same lines, we can tell whether the star is moving toward or away from the earth and how fast.

CHAPTER

3

The Earth and
Its Atmosphere

The earth is one of the sun's family of planets and to ignore it would be to leave a gap in our consideration of the solar system. Further, the earth has been our observing platform for the study of astronomy. As such, we need to know its size and shape, its mass, its motions and its atmosphere and how they affect astronomical observation.

THE SIZE AND SHAPE OF THE EARTH

The idea that Columbus was the first person to believe that the earth is round is pure myth. Almost two thousand years before his time the Greeks knew from the changing appearance of the sky in various locations and from the shape of the earth's shadow during eclipses of the moon that the earth was spherical.

In 240 B.C. Eratosthenes (276-196 B.C.) noted that when the sun was farthest north it shone directly down the wells at Syene, not far from the present Assuan in southern Egypt. On the same day at Alexandria the sun's rays made an angle with a vertical pole which was equal to one-fiftieth a circumference. Assuming correctly that the sun was so distant that its rays were essentially parallel, he concluded that the 5000 stadia between the two locations must represent one-fiftieth the circumference of the earth. Unfortunately, we cannot be positive of the exact length of the stadium he used, but his value of 250,000 stadia for the earth's circumference is almost certainly accurate to within less than 5 per cent.

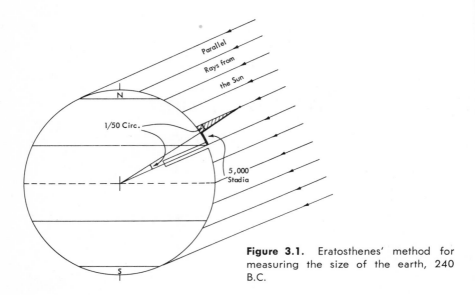

Figure 3.1. Eratosthenes' method for measuring the size of the earth, 240 B.C.

Modern observations to determine the exact size and shape of the earth employ the same two fundamental measurements that Eratosthenes made. First, the latitude and longitude of two stations are determined as exactly as possible by astronomical observations so the number of degrees in the arc of a great circle passing through the two points can be determined. Second, the linear distance between the two stations must be found. To do this, the distance between two points on a base line is directly measured with the greatest care. Using this base line as one side of several triangles, a network of triangles is laid out to reach the two astronomically determined points. By using accurate instruments to measure the interior angles of all the triangles, the length of all the sides can be computed, and finally the linear distance between two observational points can be calculated precisely. The lengths of many arcs located in all parts of the world have been measured in this way.

When the measured arcs lie along a meridian, that is, extend in a north-south direction, the length of one degree is longer near the poles than it is near the equator. In latitude 0°, the equator, one degree of latitude has a length of 68.7 miles. At Philadelphia, Peking or Madrid, in latitude 40° north, one degree has a length of 69.0 miles, and at the poles the length of one degree is 69.4 miles. The sharper curvature near the equator, indicated by the fact that one degree of latitude is a shorter linear distance there, shows the earth has an equatorial bulge. The diameter of the earth measured from pole to pole is found to be 7900 miles, and the diameter measured through the equator is 7927 miles, 1/297 greater than the polar diameter. The average of three mutually perpendicular diameters, one from pole to pole and the other two through the equator, gives a mean diameter of the earth of 7918 miles.

THE MASS OF THE EARTH

In the eighteenth century, at least two attempts were made to determine the mass of the earth by measuring how much the mass of a mountain deflected the direction of gravity in its immediate vicinity. Though the results were of the right order of magnitude, the mountain method is today considered quite inaccurate.

H. Cavendish in 1798 and P. von Jolly in 1881 obtained better results by using a balance, similar in design to the balances found in a chemistry laboratory, but much larger. Large, equally massive weights were placed on the two pans, so they were in perfect balance. Then another large mass was brought up under one of the weights. The gravitational attraction between the new mass and the mass on the pan above it caused the balance to tip slightly. Small weights were then placed on the other pan until the balance was restored. In this condition, the gravitational attraction between the two masses on, for instance, the left side of the balance must exactly equal the earth's attraction for the small weights added to the right side. Newton's law of gravitation gives the force of attraction between any two masses separated by a known distance, and since in this case the forces are equal we know that

$$\frac{G\ M_1\ M_2}{D^2} = \frac{G\ M_e\ m}{R^2} .$$

The two G's cancel out, and everything else on both sides of the equation except the mass of the earth, M_e, is known, so its value can be found.

Today, the most exact determinations of the earth's mass involve the determination of the gravitational constant, G, by means of a torsion balance. We know that the gravitational force, F, on a small mass, m, near the earth's surface is given by $F = G\ m\ M_e\ /\ R^2$ where M_e and R are the mass and the radius of the earth. We know also that if the small mass is allowed to fall freely, the force will equal the mass times the acceleration, that is $F = m\ a$. Since F is the same force in both instances we know $G\ m\ M_e\ /\ R^2 = m\ a$. Solving this equation for the mass of the earth we find that $M_e = a\ R^2 / G$. The values for the acceleration due to gravity, a, and the radius of the earth, R, are both well known. If we can determine G to a satisfactory accuracy, we can find the mass of the earth. The problem is not easy because the value of G in the centimeter-gram-second system is only about 1/15,000,000.

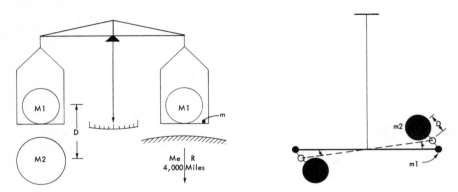

Figure 3.2. The Cavendish balance, left, gave the first reasonably accurate measurements of the earth's mass. The torsion balance, right, is used to measure the value of the gravitational constant, G.

The instrument used to determine the value of G is a torsion balance. It consists of two small balls of gold or platinum mounted at the ends of a light, horizontal quartz rod. The rod is suspended at its midpoint by a long, delicate quartz filament. When the pendulum is set oscillating in an horizontal plane, it winds and unwinds the quartz filament, but because the suspension is so delicate, the period of oscillation is quite long. By accurately timing the period of the pendulum and calculating the moment of inertia of the bar and balls, it is possible to determine how much force is needed to twist the suspension through, for example, one degree. Two larger balls are now brought up near the ends of the pendulum bar in such a position that their attraction will produce a slight twist in the suspension. The amount of twist is a measure of the gravitational force between the large balls and those on the pendulum, so the gravitational constant G can be determined directly from $F = G\ m_1\ m_2 / D^2$.

Using this method the mass of the earth was measured at the National Bureau of Standards by Dr. Paul Heyl and found to be 6.6×10^{21} (6600 million million million) tons.[1]

---

[1]Exponential notation, such as 6.6×10^{21}, is a convenient way to express large numbers. It indicates that the decimal point should be moved to the right by the number of places indicated by the exponent of 10. Thus 6.6×10^{21} is the same as 6,600,000,000,000,000,000,000.

THE DENSITY OF THE EARTH

The average density of any body is simply its total mass divided by its total volume. The mass of the earth has been measured to be 13.2 x 10^{24} pounds, and its volume, calculated from the measured radius, is 3.84 x 10^{22} cubic feet. Thus, the mean density of the earth is 344 pounds per cubic foot, or 5.5 times the density of water.

Since the average density of surface rocks of the earth is only about 2.7 times the density of water, there must be regions in the interior in which the density is far above the average. Man's greatest penetration into the earth's crust has been in the drilling of oil wells, and the deepest of these is down slightly over 5 miles, only 1/8 of one per cent of the earth's radius. Clearly, we have learned little about the earth's interior by direct observation, but from the way in which the waves set up by earthquakes travel through the interior of the earth, seismologists have been able to gain a reasonably complete understanding of the density and rigidity of the materials comprising the earth's interior. Current indications are that the material at the center of the earth has a density about sixteen times the density of water, or half a ton per cubic foot.

It seems likely that the earth's core contains a high percentage of iron, but recent work indicates that for every million hydrogen atoms in the solar system there are only five or six iron atoms. Possible explanations of this remarkable concentration of heavy material in the interior of the earth will be considered in Chapter 7.

THE EARTH'S ATMOSPHERE

From an astronomical standpoint, the gases which make up the earth's atmosphere must be considered an integral part of the earth. Held down by the earth's gravitational pull, they have a sea-level pressure of about 14.7 pounds per square inch. If we multiply this value by the area of the earth's surface in square inches, we find that the weight of the earth's atmosphere is 5600 million million tons, roughly 1/1,000,000 the total mass of the earth. A cubic foot of air at sea level weighs about 1.2 ounces.

The atmospheric pressure decreases so rapidly with elevation that at a height of about 19,000 feet the pressure is only half the sea-level value. Compared with the size of the earth, this is an extremely thin layer. On a 6-inch globe this would be less than the thickness of one of the pages in this book. The pressure and density continue to decrease rapidly with elevation, reducing by about half for each 4 miles in elevation, so that about 97 per cent of our atmosphere is within 20 miles of sea level. The total extent of our atmosphere is largely a matter of definition, but at a height of only 70 miles the pressure is reduced to

1/1,000,000 the sea-level value. Auroras have been observed as high as 600 to 700 miles, indicating that traces of the atmosphere must extend to this level. At still higher elevations, our atmosphere must blend imperceptibly with the occasional gas molecules which probably populate interplanetary space.

The chemical constitution of our atmosphere is remarkably and surprisingly uniform over all parts of the earth to heights of at least 100 miles. Our air is made up of 78 per cent nitrogen and 21 per cent oxygen, with the remaining one per cent composed largely of argon, a small amount of carbon dioxide and minute quantities of many other gases. The air may contain up to 4 per cent water vapor; it is from this atmospheric moisture that all the precipitation of the world originates. In the layer between 10 and 20 miles above sea level, there is an interesting concentration of ozone, the molecule made of three oxygen atoms. Though the concentration is only about 1 part in 5 million, it is of vital importance because it absorbs about 98 per cent of the ultraviolet light coming from the sun. If it were not for the ozone in the atmosphere, we would experience violent sunburn and severe eye damage.

In the lower several miles of our atmosphere the temperature of the air decreases, on the average, at the rate of 3.6° F per 1000 feet. This is a general average and should not be taken to represent the specific situation at any particular place or time. Somewhat surprisingly, the temperature of the air does not continue to drop with elevation. Though the exact values vary somewhat seasonally and at various latitudes on the earth, rocket soundings indicate that the temperature drops to about −60°F at elevations between 10 and 15 miles, then rises to about +60°F at 35 miles, drops again to a low of close to −150°F at heights of about 50 miles and then climbs to a temperature of 1000°F or more at elevations of several hundred miles. It is important to recognize that these are kinetic temperatures, based on the speeds with which the gas molecules are moving. At these higher elevations there are so few molecules that the actual heat content of the atmosphere would be extremely low.

The Van Allen Layers

The United States artificial satellite, Explorer I, launched on January 31, 1958, detected a zone of charged particles moving at extremely high speeds at elevations of a few thousand miles above the earth's surface. Subsequent investigations by artificial satellites and space probes revealed the existence of a second zone of concentration. The inner zone is approximatly 3000 miles thick and reaches its greatest intensity at an elevation of about 2000 miles above the earth's equator. The outer zone seems to be 4000 to 6000 miles thick, centered at an elevation of 10,000 to 12,000 miles. Both zones apparently surround the earth like wide, flattened belts which, following the earth's magnetic field, are highest over the equator and dip quite low in polar regions. They are named for Professor James A. Van Allen, of the University of Iowa, who directed the radiation-detecting experiments.

The origin of these charged particles is not yet entirely clear. They may originate as charged particles reaching the earth in the form of a corpuscular radiation from the sun. It is quite possible that some of the particles, particularly in the inner belt, are formed from molecules in the earth's upper atmosphere that have been hit by cosmic rays. However they are formed, the charged particles are accelerated to high velocities in the earth's magnetic field. Prolonged exposure to these high energy particles might prove to be dangerous, but current investigations would seem to indicate that a space traveler who passed through the zones in a relatively short time would not be subjected to a dangerous amount of radiation.

Insolation and the Seasons

Less than one two-billionth the energy radiated by the sun is intercepted by the earth, and roughly half that is turned away by our atmosphere. The part that does get through, however, is enough to make the earth a habitable planet.

If a surface one centimeter square is exposed to the solar radiation at the earth's mean distance from the sun, and outside our atmosphere, it will receive energy at the rate of 1.94 calories per minute. This quantity is known as the solar constant, though actually it is slightly variable.

The earth rotates on its axis once each day and revolves around the sun once a year. If the earth's orbit were perfectly circular and if the earth's axis were exactly perpendicular to the plane of the orbit, days and nights would be of equal length all over the earth, and there would be no seasonal changes. The earth's orbit, however, is slightly elliptical, so we are more than 3 million miles closer to the sun in early January than we are early in July. Thus, our planet as a whole receives about 6 per cent more radiation in the middle of our northern winter than it does during the hottest days of our summer. Obviously, our distance from the sun is not the major cause of seasons.

The earth's axis is tilted 23°27′ away from the perpendicular to the plane of its orbit, a figure known with remarkable accuracy to the ancient Greeks. As the earth revolves around the sun once each year, the axis remains parallel to its former positions. (Actually, precession causes the earth's axis to maintain the same angle with the plane of its orbit, but to swing around with a slow conical motion once every 25,800 years.

The motion is thus much too slow to be significant in our discussion of the cause of seasons.) On about June 21 each year the North Pole is tilted most sharply toward the sun, and around December 21 it is tilted farthest away. On about March 21 and September 21 each year the plane of the earth's equator will pass through the sun, and the sunlight will graze both poles tangentially. To an observer on the earth, the sun will seem to move farther and farther north during the spring, until on June 21 it will be shining perpendicularly down on a spot in latitude 23°27′ North. After that date it will appear to drift to the south until on about December 21 it will be shining perpendicularly on 23°27′ South latitude. These latitudes establish the Tropic of Cancer and the Tropic of Capricorn, respectively.

Outside the tropics the sun never passes directly overhead, but its changing position can cause a wide variation in the amount of insolation received at different times of the year. For example, at Chicago on June 21 the sun passes within 18°21′ of the zenith at noon, and the insolation is 95 per cent as strong as if the sun were exactly overhead. In addition, on that day the sun is above the horizon for 15 hours 13 minutes. By contrast, on December 21 the highest point in the sun's path at Chicago is less than 25 degrees above the horizon, so the surface of the earth there is receiving only 42 per cent as intense radiation as it would if the sun were directly overhead. Furthermore, the day, from sunrise to sunset, lasts for only 9 hours and 8 minutes. In that latitude the surface of the earth receives more than three and a half times as much heat on June 21 as it does on December 21.

From the preceding discussion it might appear that the highest and lowest temperatures should occur in late June and late December. Actually, the hottest and coldest days occur about six weeks after the solstices. The earth not only receives heat from the sun but also radiates heat, and the rate of radiation is proportional to the fourth power of the absolute temperature of the earth at the time and place under consideration. Any change in the temperature of a region of the earth will depend on whether it is receiving more energy than it is radiating or is radiating more than receiving. The temperature of the earth is comparable to the balance in a checking account. If the deposits exceed the withdrawals the balance gets larger; if the withdrawals are greater than the deposits the balance decreases.

At any point north of the Tropic of Cancer the earth receives its maximum insolation on June 21, but the ground will not have warmed enough to radiate away as much heat as it is receiving. Under these conditions the temperature will continue to rise. Though the incoming radiation will diminish slowly after June 21, and the rate of radiation from the earth will increase slowly as the ground becomes warmer, the two will not become equal until early in August. It is then that we can expect the hottest weather. After that time the earth will be losing more heat than it receives, and we may expect the temperatures to start down. A comparable situation occurs in the winter. The Northern Hemisphere receives its minimum insolation at the time of the winter solstice, about December 21, but the ground is still warm enough to radiate more energy than it receives until early in February, when the lowest temperatures can be expected. This delay of about six weeks between the times of the maximum and minimum insolation and the dates of the maximum and minimum temperature is known as the lag of the seasons.

SUMMARY

This chapter has touched very briefly on a number of topics related to the earth which are expanded to much greater detail in the Earth Science Series, but through the centuries as astronomical measurements have established the size and shape, mass and density, the atmospheric characteristics and the nature and cause of the temperatures and seasons on the earth, it could be contended that astronomers have laid much of the groundwork for the modern study of the earth sciences.

The Moon

TOPICS

Phases of the moon   The lunar surface
Conditions on the moon   Eclipses

Though the full moon is about half a million times fainter than the sun, it is over twenty thousand times as bright as the brighest star, and nearly two thousand times as bright as Venus. It has been known since the dawn of human intelligence, and its changing phases probably are responsible for our seven-day week and definitely are the basis for our twenty-eight to thirty-one day months. Primitive man regarded the moon with superstitious awe, but it was treated as an object of scientific interest as far back as the time of the Greeks. Through the centuries that interest has grown apace with our developing instrumentation. During the past decade the moon has, quite literally, rocketed into a position of prominence.

The diameter of the moon is 2159 miles, roughly one fourth the diameter of the earth, and its mass is about 1/81 that of the earth. Though it is exceeded in size by four other satellites in the solar system, it is much larger in comparison with its primary than any of the others. It has even been suggested that perhaps the earth and moon should be considered to be a double planet, rather than a planet and a satellite.

As the moon orbits around the center of gravity of the earth-moon system each month, its distance from our planet varies from 221,463 to 252,710 miles, averaging a little under a quarter of a million miles, or very nearly sixty times the radius of the earth. With respect to the stars, the moon rotates on its axis in exactly the same length of time it revolves around the planet, causing the same side of the moon to face the earth at all times. Because the moon's axis is not exactly perpendicular to the plane of its orbit, because its orbital speed is not constant and because we can observe from widely separated points on the earth, our telescopes have been able to reach about 59 per cent of the moon's surface. Photographic mapping of the remaining 41 per cent from orbiting space vehicles is nearing completion.

Two different time intervals are given for the moon's period of revolution around the earth. The sideral month has a length of twenty-seven and one-third days and is the time required for the moon to circle the earth once with respect to the fixed stars. Its eastward motion is thus 13.2 degrees per day when compared to the stellar background. However, during the sideral month the earth-moon system will have advanced about 27 degrees in the orbit around the sun, so the moon will not have completed one revolution with respect to the line joining the sun and earth. Slightly over two days more are needed for the moon to occupy the same position in relation to the sun and earth and thus return to the same phase that it had at the beginning of the period. The synodic month, or month of the phases, is twenty-nine and one-half days in length, causing the moon to gain on the sun at the rate of 12.2 degrees per day.

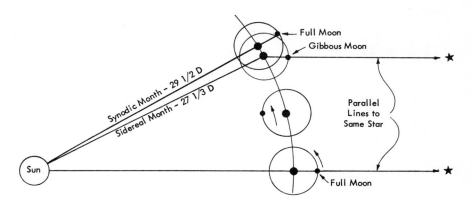

Figure 4.1. The synodic month of the phases is more than two days longer than the sidereal month measured by the stars.

The appearance of the moon in the sky is misleading. It has about the same apparent angular diameter as the sun, so there is a tendency to think of them as being about equally far from the earth. Actually, the distance to the moon is only 1/400 the distance to the sun. A scale model which placed the earth one mile from the sun would have a sun 50 feet in diameter, the earth would be 5½ inches in diameter, and the moon, circling the earth at a distance of 13 feet, would be 1½ inches in diameter.

THE PHASES OF THE MOON

We see the moon because of the sunlight falling on it. At new moon, when it is close to the line joining the earth to the sun, it is the side which is away from us that is being illuminated. As the moon revolves around the earth, moving to the east with respect to the sun at the rate of 12.2 degrees each day, we see more and more of the illuminated half. For the first week after new moon, it will show a crescent phase, and during the second week it will be gibbous. After full moon it goes through the

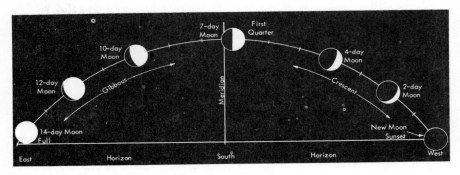

Figure 4.2. As the angle between the sun and the moon increases we see more of the moon's surface on which the sun is shining.

gibbous and crescent phases in reverse order, rising, on the average, about 50 minutes later each evening. Just before the next new moon, the old crescent moon will be rising in the eastern predawn sky only an hour or two before the sun.

As seen from the moon, the earth would show similar phases but would appear nearly four times as large in diameter as the moon looks from the earth. Also, because of our atmosphere and clouds, the earth is a much better reflector than the moon, and thus earth light on the moon averages about eighty times as strong as the moonlight on the earth. Because of the intensity of this light reflected by the earth, a faint disk of the entire moon can frequently be seen cradled in the crescent.

CONDITIONS ON THE MOON

The moon has no detectable atmosphere. When the moon passes in front of a star there is no dimming such as would occur if the light had to pass through a layer of gas. The stars remain at full brilliance and then disappear instantaneously as the moon moves across the line of sight. No scattering of light appears in the shadows of the lunar mountains. Though a few observers have suspected color changes in some of the deeper craters, there have been no observations of anything resembling clouds floating in a lunar atmosphere. Spectra of the moon are identical with the spectra of the sun. No new lines have been added.

Theoretical considerations support the observational evidence. The force of gravity on the moon is only one sixth as strong as the force of gravity on the earth so any particle moving more than 1 1/2 miles per second would escape the moon's gravitational field. If the moon could be given an atmosphere identical to the earth's the gas molecules would have velocities well above the velocity of escape, and within a few months the moon would again be without air. Any gases given off by the solid material of the moon would similarly escape and any water would evaporate to form gas molecules which the moon would be unable to hold. Since the moon has no air and no water it obviously can have no life.

The period of rotation of the moon with respect to the sun is equal to its synodic period, twenty-nine and one-half days. Except for modifications in the polar regions, any point on the moon will experience a day that is more than two weeks of our time in length, followed by an equally long night. With no air or clouds to turn back part of the solar radiation, the surface temperatures on the day side climb to about 265°F. At night, with no atmosphere to hold the heat, the temperature must go down to approximately −300°F. Near the sunrise and sunset regions the temperatures are probably more like those we experience on the earth.

THE LUNAR SURFACE

Even a naked-eye view of the moon is sufficient to show that its surface is not completely uniform. Darker and lighter areas can be seen which are imagined to form the man in the moon or the lady in the moon. A small telescope or even good binoculars reveal a wealth of detail. Large, relatively smooth plains, called maria, though they are not seas, appear to be somewhat darker than the rest of the lunar surface. The brighter areas appear covered with craters ranging in size from 100 miles in diameter down to the limit of resolution of the instrument being used. Photographs taken by recent lunar probes indicate that some of the smallest craters may be only a few feet across. In certain areas, mountain ranges hundreds of miles long extend across the lunar surface. A few vertical cliffs, one, the Straight Wall, 600 feet high and 80 miles long, suggest faulting. Around the time of a full moon, rays of lighter-colored material approximately 10 miles wide and many hundreds of miles long can be seen radiating from several of the larger craters.

With large telescopes or space probes the maria are found not to be as smooth as they appear in small instruments. Their color, low reflectivity and relative smoothness suggest that they might be old lava flows, and a few jagged mountain peaks which protrude support this suggestion. It is hard to understand, however, how a body as small as the moon could have developed pressures and temperatures high enough to have produced lava flows on such a large scale. Highly detailed photographs reveal a slightly undulating surface liberally sprinkled with small, rounded craters. Our first lunar landing party will probably be able to definitely establish the nature of these regions.

The areas not covered by the maria are lighter in color and look like a jumbled wilderness of craters, with smaller ones breaking through the rims of larger ones. Not infrequently there is a mountain peak in the center of the crater floor. Usually, the rim rises above the surrounding terrain, with the inner slope steeper than the outside, and with the relatively smooth crater floor sometimes higher and sometimes lower than the general lunar topography. In size they run from tiny, barely visible pits to walled plains 100 miles and more across. In height, the more rugged are comparable to the mountains on the earth.

The origin of the lunar craters has been and still is the subject of much discussion. One group argues for something resembling volcanic origin, and a single Russian observation of the spectrum of gases in one of the craters tends to uphold this thesis; however, they certainly do not resemble the small craters and large cinder cones of many terrestrial volcanoes.

Another large group contends that the craters are meteoric, similar to the Barringer crater in Arizona. They argue that both the moon and the earth suffered a violent storm of large meteoids in the distant past and that the airless climate on the moon preserved its craters, while those of the earth were either eroded away, or perhaps because of its greater mass, the earth had not solidified enough to retain the markings. Unless, and this seems unlikely, the meteoric impacts were so violent in certain areas that they melted the surface material, the meteoric theory is hardpressed to explain the maria. Perhaps both theories are partially

Figure 4.3. The full moon shows no shadows, but lunar rays can be seen extending from some of the larger craters. At first quarter the sunrise portion near the terminator shows the mountains, craters and maria clearly. Lick Observatory photographs.

Figure 4.4. The crater Clavius is shown in remarkable detail in this photograph taken with the 200-inch Hale Telescope. Photograph from the Mount Wilson and Palomar Observatories.

right, or perhaps they are both wrong. Again, our first field party on the moon may come up with the answer.

Even without the wind and water erosion which is present on the earth it had been assumed that the extreme temperature changes and billions of meteoric impacts on the moon's surface would produce a layer of dust, variously estimated to be from a few inches to several tens of feet thick. In the few isolated areas of recent soft landings on the moon, however, the surface seems to have load-bearing and cohesive characteristics similar to damp beach sand. With no air, dry particles may stick together in much the same way that damp granules do on the earth.

ECLIPSES

It is an interesting and fortunate coincidence that the distances and diameters of the sun and moon are such that they have the same apparent angular diameters in the sky. In fact, both distances vary enough that the moon sometimes looks larger and sometimes smaller than the sun.

If the plane of the moon's orbit coincided with the plane of the earth's orbit, there would be an eclipse of the sun at every new moon and an eclipse of the moon at every full moon. Actually, the moon's orbital plane is inclined 5° 9′ to the plane of the earth's orbit, so eclipses take place only when a new moon or full moon occurs reasonably close to the intersection of the two orbital planes. As the earth-moon system revolves around the sun each year, the intersection of the two orbital planes, or line of nodes, will point to the sun only twice, and we therefore normally have two eclipse seasons each year. Strictly speaking, the line of nodes does not remain exactly parallel to its former positions but backs around a full 360 degrees every 18.6 years. Thus, the eclipse year, or the interval between the instants that the line of nodes points to the sun on the same side of the earth's orbit, is 346.6 days. It is therefore possible to have two full eclipse seasons and part of a third in one calendar year.

If a new moon occurs close enough to the line of nodes, the disk of the moon will cover all or part of the sun, and we experience a solar eclipse. Because the sun is so much larger than the moon, the moon's umbra, or total shadow, is a long, tapering cone. Under the most favorable conditions it can be only 167 miles wide where it intersects the earth's surface. The moon is moving toward the east about 2000 miles an hour in its orbit, but the earth's rotation carries a point on the equator to the east about 1000 miles an hour. Thus, the long finger-like shadow of the moon sweeps eastward across the earth's surface at a speed of 1000 miles an hour or more. Only if an observer is within this path of totality

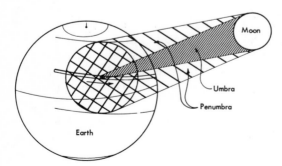

Figure 4.5. The tip of the umbra sweeps across the earth, producing a total eclipse path less than 167 miles wide but thousands of miles long.

will he see a total eclipse, and under the most favorable conditions it can last only 7.5 minutes. If the moon is farther away, the shadow path will be narrower and the eclipse of shorter duration. It often happens that the moon is so distant that the point of its shadow cannot reach the earth. Under these conditions an observer, even if he is exactly on the central line, will find that the moon appears smaller than the sun, and at the middle of the eclipse a thin ring of the sun can be seen all around the moon's disk. This is an annular eclipse. Frequently, the umbra does not touch the earth at all, but the surrounding partial shadow, the penumbra, does; or, the observer may be outside the path of totality, but within the region of the penumbra. In this case, he sees only a partial eclipse, with the moon's disk moving across the sun off center so that it never becomes central.

Figure 4.6. The solar corona photographed at Fryeburg, Maine, August 31, 1932. Lick Observatory photograph.

A total solar eclipse is one of the most spectacular of natural phenomena. About an hour before totality, an observer watching through two or three thicknesses of heavily exposed photographic film (viewing an eclipse without suitable protection for the eyes can cause irreparable damage) will see the moon slowly move onto the face of the sun from the western side. When the disk is almost covered, the daylight dims noticeably, and during the last few seconds darkness comes on with astonishing rapidity. Just before the last thin crescent of the sun disappears, the surface of the earth seems to be covered with wavering shadow bands. In the final seconds before the sun is completely covered, it may show only through low valleys on the edge of the moon, producing Bailey's Beads. Then the corona flashes into view, pearly white on the outside, and slightly yellow near the sun. Brilliant red prominences may be seen extending upward into the inner corona. For a few brief seconds, or at most a few minutes, one can only gaze in awe. If an astronomer is taking scientific photographs he may be so busy changing plates and timing exposures that he can only steal a few quick glances at the eclipse he has traveled thousands of miles to observe. Then, with astonishing suddenness the eclipse is over. Bailey's Beads and the shadow bands come and go in quick succession, and as the first thin rim of the sun appears it seems blindingly bright. Quickly the daylight strengthens, slowly the moon moves off the face of the sun, and in another hour that eclipse has become history.

Eclipses of the moon occur when the full moon passes through the earth's shadow. Though they are less spectacular and less valuable scientifically than solar eclipses, they are well-worth watching. As the full moon moves into the penumbra of the earth's shadow the dimming is so gradual that it is scarcely noticeable, but as it moves into the umbra a definite dark shadow with a slightly soft edge seems to darken the eastern limb of the moon. The earth's shadow is about 5700 miles in diameter at the moon's distance, so the arc of the shadow seen on the full moon is always much less sharply curved than the edge of the moon itself. The fact that the edge of the shadow was always the arc of a circle was recognized by the Greeks as a proof that the earth was spherical. If the moon is passing centrally through the umbra, it will take about an hour for the shadow to completely cover the moon. Totality will last for about 1 hour and 40 minutes. Rarely, as in the eclipse of December 30, 1963, does the moon disappear completely from view. During most eclipses the earth's atmosphere refracts enough red light into the umbra to permit the entire moon to be seen as a dull, brick-red disk. At the end of totality, as the moon moves from the umbra into the penumbra, the eastern edge brightens, and for about an hour the long curved line

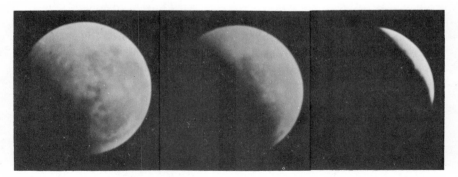

Figure 4.7. The moon partially eclipsed. Notice that the edge of the earth's shadow is the arc of a circle. Yerkes Observatory photograph.

of the shadow edge moves across the face of the moon. If the moon does not go through the center of the shadow, the partial phases will be longer, but the time of totality will be considerably shortened.

There must be at least one solar eclipse, total, annular or partial, at each eclipse season. Thus, we must have at least two solar eclipses each year. It is possible to have two solar eclipses in each eclipse season, and with a part of a third eclipse season occurring occasionally within the same calendar year, the maximum number of solar eclipses in any one year is five. The limits for umbral lunar eclipses are narrower, so there can never be more than one in any eclipse season, and it is possible to get by a season with no lunar eclipse. Thus, the maximum number of lunar eclipses in a calendar year is three, and the minimum is none. The limits are so close that it is not possible to have five solar and three lunar eclipses in the same year. The maximum number of both kinds is seven, three of the moon and four of the sun, or two of the moon and five of the sun.

SUMMARY

In terms of the whole astronomical universe it must be admitted that the moon is relatively insignificant. It is just a small, airless, waterless, lifeless body, without heat or light of its own, and with even its motion through space controlled by the sun and the earth; however, it has played an important part in the lives of men on the earth. It has lighted the night and established the calendar. Its eclipses lead to an understanding of the true shape of the earth. Perhaps most important of all, it has caused men to wonder what it is and where it came from.

There is a Chinese proverb which says, "A journey of a thousand miles begins with a single step." Our first step in the manned exploration of space is to be a landing party on the moon.

5

The Planets in the Solar System

TOPICS

Planetary motions   The sun's planets

PLANETARY MOTIONS

No one knows how early in human history it was first noticed that among the thousands of stars which maintained their positions relative to each other there were a few objects, looking much like stars, which appeared to move. These planets (the word *planet* means "wanderer") were the source of much bewilderment. They were confined to a relatively narrow belt only 16 degrees wide in the sky. Usually their motion was direct, that is, in an easterly direction, but periodically each of them would retrograde, or move in a westerly direction.

Many of the early Greeks tried to explain the apparently erratic motions of the planets. Ptolemy, in A.D. 140, suggested the explanation which was generally accepted for about fourteen centuries. He assumed that the earth was stationary and that the motion of each of the planets could be explained by a system of circles. A point, moving on the circumference of a large circle whose center was near the earth, became the center of a second circle. A point moving on this circle became the center of a third and so on, until first five and later six circles were used to explain the motions of each of the planets. The system was complicated and clumsy and made no attempt to say why the planets moved as they did, but it was accepted until well into the sixteenth century.

In 1543, Copernicus published his *De Revolutionibus Orbium Celestium;* in it he held that each of the then-known planets, Mercury, Venus, Earth, Mars, Jupiter and Saturn, in the order of their increasing distance from the sun, went around the sun in a circular orbit. His main contention was that the sun, since it was so much larger and more important than the earth, must be the center of the planetary system. He pointed out that the observation of moving planets from a moving earth would provide a relatively simple explanation of their apparent direct and retrograde motions. Unfortunately, Copernicus felt he had to use circular orbits and constant speeds, and thus he had to employ epicycles to obtain the desired accuracy in the prediction of planetary positions. The gradual acceptance of the Copernican theory did, however, free men's thinking from the highly restricting assumption that the earth was the center of the entire universe.

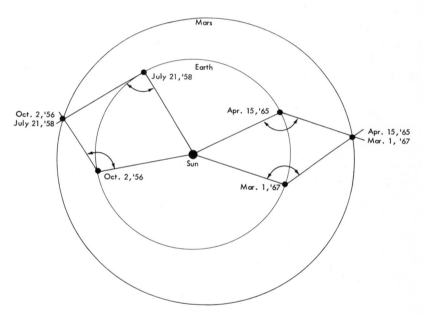

Figure 5.1. If lines are drawn from the earth to Mars at two times, separated by the exact interval required for Mars to complete one circuit of its orbit and return to the identical position, they will intersect at a point on Mars' orbit.

Johannes Kepler (1571-1630) was a German mathematical astronomer who worked with Tycho Brahe (1546-1601), a Danish nobleman, and probably the finest astronomical observer the world had seen. Kepler tried to fit Tycho's accurate observations to the planetary positions predicted by the Copernican system, but found the differences too large to be acceptable. However, by plotting the positions of Mars as determined from Tycho's observations, he discovered that the orbit of Mars was not a circle, but an ellipse, and that the sun was located not at the center but at one of the foci. He further noted that Mars moved more rapidly in its orbit when it was closest to the sun, at perihelion, than when it was most distant, at aphelion. Thus, in 1609, Kepler published his first two laws of planetary motion.

1. *The law of elliptical orbit*: The orbit of every planet is an ellipse with the sun at one of the foci.
2. *The law of equal areas*: A line joining any planet to the sun sweeps over equal areas in equal intervals of time.

When the Copernican theory was revised to include elliptical orbits and variable speeds within the orbits, all epicycles were eliminated and the theory predicted the observed positions perfectly.

In another publication nine years later, Kepler stated the third of his laws of planetary motion.

3. *The harmonic law*: The squares of the periods of revolution of any two planets around the sun are in the same proportion as the cubes of their mean distances from the sun.

By its use, if the sidereal period of revolution of any planet is known, its mean distance from the sun can be found; or if its mean distance is known, its period of revolution is directly obtainable.

It is important to recognize that at the time of their publication, Kepler's three laws were merely empirical rules which described how the planets moved. The scientific world had to wait more than half a century for Newton's law of gravitation to provide the explanation of why the planets obeyed Kepler's laws.

Sir Isaac Newton (1643-1727) is generally recognized as the greatest scientist that had lived up to his time, and he will continue to be recognized as one of the truly great scientists of all times. His three laws of motion and his law of universal gravitation were probably developed during the period around 1666, though they were not published until 1687 in his *Philosophiae Naturalis Principia Mathematica*, commonly called simply the *Principia*.

Newton's three laws of motion give a clear statement of the relationship between masses, forces and accelerations. They form the basis of the entire field of mechanics and are, for example, the starting point for calculation of the orbits of artificial satellites and space probes. In the order in which Newton stated them they are as follows:

1. Every body persists in a state of rest or uniform motion in a straight line unless it is compelled to change that state by a force impressed upon it.
2. The acceleration is directly proportional to the force and inversely proportional to the mass of the body and takes place in the direction of the straight line in which the force acts.
3. To every action there is always an equal and contrary reaction.

In his *Principia* Newton also gave his law of gravitation, stating that between any two bodies in the universe there is a force which is directly proportional to the product of their masses and inversely proportional to the square of the distance between them. In equation form it becomes:

$$F = \frac{G \ m_1 \ m_2}{D^2}$$

If the two masses, m_1 and m_2, are in grams, the distance between them, D, is in centimeters, and the force F is in dynes, the gravitational constant, G, has a value of about 1/15,000,000. Here, for the first time, was the explanation of why the planets move in elliptical orbits around the sun, why their orbital velocity is greater when they are near perihelion than when they are near aphelion, and why their periods of revolution become longer with increasing distance from the sun.

THE SUN'S PLANETS

The sun has a family of nine known planets which revolve around it in a counterclockwise direction as seen from the north. All the planetary orbits are elliptical, but most of them have such a small eccentricity that they would appear almost circular to the eye. With the exception of Pluto, the planes of all the planetary orbits lie within 7 degrees of the plane of the earth's orbit.

For distances within the solar system, it is convenient to call the average distance from the sun to the earth, about 92,960,000 miles, one Astronomical Unit (A.U.). The distances of the various planets from the sun range from 0.4 A.U. to almost 40 A.U. and their periods of revolution around the sun are as short as eighty-eight days and as long as 248.4 years.

Many of the vital statistics for the various planets are collected in Table 1. Since the origin of the earth cannot be separated from the origin of the rest of the solar system, we will look briefly at those characteristics of the various planets which must be satisfactorily explained by any tenable theory of their origin.

Mercury is the nearest known planet to the sun and, with a diameter of only 3100 miles, is probably the smallest. At its mean distance of 36 million miles, it is only 0.4 A.U. from the sun, resulting in solar radiation about seven times as strong as we receive. Until a few years ago, it was believed to always keep the same side facing the sun, but recent radar observations seem to indicate a period of rotation equal to about sixty earth days. The side facing ihe sun must become extremely hot, probably about 660°F, or higher than the melting points of tin and lead, while on the night side the temperature is around −450°F, not far above absolute zero. Strange as it may seem, this little planet may experience both the highest and the lowest temperatures found on any of the planets in the solar system.

The nature of the atmospheres of the various planets will be of considerable significance later on when we consider theories about the formation of the solar system. Mercury has no atmosphere, and the reasons are quite clear. Its mass is only 1/20 the mass of the earth, which, coupled with its small size, gives it a surface gravity about 1/3 as strong as we experience. Under these conditions, a particle such as a gas molecule that had a velocity only slightly over 2 miles a second would be able to escape entirely from Mercury's gravitational field. With temperatures well above 600°F, a large proportion of the molecules in any atmosphere which Mercury might have had would be moving with speeds considerably above the critical velocity of escape and would thus leave the planet, never to return. As the more slowly moving molecules became heated or acquired high velocities through collision with other atmospheric particles, they too would escape, and within a remarkably short time Mercury would be left without an atmosphere.

Mercury's sidereal period of revolution around the sun, that is, its period with respect to the fixed stars, is eighty-eight days, but because the earth is also moving, Mercury's synodic period, or the interval required for it to gain a lap on the earth, is one hundred sixteen days. Being much closer to the sun than we are, Mercury can never appear more than 28 degrees away from the sun as we see them in the sky. Daytime observations are quite unsatisfactory, and at night Mercury can only be seen very low in the western sky just after sunset, or very low in the eastern sky just before sunrise. At these times it looks about as large as a dime seen at a distance of nearly 1/3 a mile, but of course, only the half which is facing the sun is illuminated. When it is almost on a line between the earth and the sun, it appears considerably larger, but in that position we cannot see the illuminated side. When it is far beyond the sun in the most distant part of its orbit from the earth, we see the entire face illuminated, but its great distance makes the planet appear very small, and it is located so close to the sun that night observations are impossible.

The major axis of Mercury's orbit, its line of apsides, has been known for a long time to be rotating at the rate of 574 seconds of arc per century. Of this total, 531 seconds could be accounted for by the perturbations of the other planets in the solar system. For a time it was thought that the unexplained 43 seconds per century might be caused by an unknown planet located closer to the sun than Mercury, but Einstein's general theory of relativity, published in 1916, not only predicted that a body moving in an orbit in a strong gravitational field would experience a shift of its line of apsides, but even predicted for Mercury a shift of 43 seconds per century, in perfect agreement with the observations. This was the first experimental verification of the validity of the general theory of relativity. Some recent work suggests that a slight equatorial bulge on the sun may account for a few seconds per century in the motion of Mercury's orbit. Present indications are that the effect is far too small to constitute a serious threat to the relativity verification.

Venus is the second planet out from the sun. Its orbit is the most nearly circular of any of the planets, and as a result, its distance from the sun varies by less than half a million miles from its mean value of 67.3 million miles. The sidereal period of Venus is two hundred twenty-five days, but it requires a little over a year and seven months to "lap" the earth. When Venus is between the earth and the sun, its distance from

us can be as little as 25 million miles, but on the far side of its orbit its distance exceeds 160 million. When Venus is seen as a thin crescent near its minimum distance, its apparent angular diameter is more than six times as great as when it is seen fully illuminated at its maximum distance. In 1610, Galileo discovered that Venus showed phases similar to the phases of the moon, but he did not announce it openly for fear of incurring the further displeasure of church officials. He did, however, publish a sentence which was an anagram of a statement that Venus had an appearance similar to the moon. Thus, by simply reveal-

Figure 5.2. Venus near inferior conjunction is seen as a thin crescent. Photographed from Mount Wilson and Palomar Observatories.

ing the solution to his anagram he could establish his priority in the discovery.

Venus' diameter of 7700 miles and mass of 0.82 of the earth's mass make it much more nearly like the earth than any of the other planets. Its internal structure could be similar to that of the earth. Venus definitely has an atmosphere which, though probably not too thick in terms of miles, is so dense that we have never been able to observe the actual surface of the planet. As a result, its period of rotation is somewhat uncertain. If it were as short as two weeks it could be measured by means of the Doppler shift. Some have suggested that Venus keeps the same face toward the sun at all times, but if this were true we would expect the difference between the temperatures on the day side and night side to be greater than is observed. Recent radar observations indicate that the planet probably has a slow rotation once in every two hundred forty-seven earth days in a clockwise direction, opposite to its direction of revolution around the sun. Further space probes will undoubtedly provide more information within the near future.

The atmosphere of Venus seems to be completely cloudy, though the nature of the clouds has not been definitely established. The spectroscope reveals a high concentration of carbon dioxide, and recent observations suggest the strong possibility of carbon monoxide and nitrogen as well. Little free oxygen has been found, but oxygen would probably have combined with other elements unless it were being continually released by plant life. Observations from balloons drifting above 98 per cent of the earth's atmosphere reveal an appreciable amount of water vapor in the atmosphere of Venus.

Direct measurements of the strength of the infrared radiation show a temperature of between $-27°$ and $-45°F$ for both the daylight and dark sides of the planet. This radiation probably originates fairly high in the atmosphere. Measurements of the strength of the radio frequency radiation from Venus indicate a temperature of approximately $+640°F$. This radiation is believed to originate at the surface of the planet, and if there is something in the nature of the greenhouse effect that tends to trap energy beneath the upper levels of the atmosphere, this temperature is not unreasonable.

Because of the size of its orbit, Venus can never appear more than 47 degrees away from the sun. Under favorable conditions, this allows the astronomer several hours of good observing when Venus is in the western sky after sunset, or in the eastern sky before sunrise.

Except for the sun and the moon, Venus is the most brilliant object in the sky. Its high reflectivity, its nearness to the sun and, at times, its nearness to the earth enable it to reach an apparent magnitude of about

—4.4, or thirteen times as bright as the brightest star. At these times the light from Venus is strong enough to cast noticeable shadows.

Earth, at a mean distance of 92.9 million miles from the sun, is the third planet in the sun's family. The earth and the moon have already been considered in some detail and are mentioned here only to emphasize their place in the solar system.

Mars, at a mean distance of 1.52 A.U. from the sun, can come within 35 million miles of the earth, closer than any planet except Venus. When Mars is closest to us it is in opposition, that is, directly opposite the sun. It then rises about the time the sun sets, remains in the sky all night and sets at dawn. Because its orbit is quite eccentric, Mars' distance from the sun varies by 26 million miles. For oppositions that occur in August, Mars will be at the nearest point to the sun in its orbit, and we will enjoy a "favorable opposition," or closest approach to the planet. For oppositions occurring in February, Mars will be over 60 million miles from the earth at its nearest approach.

Mars is 4140 miles in diameter, slightly more than half as large as the earth, and its mass is only 1/9 that of the earth. Its day is just 37 minutes longer than ours, and its axis is tilted 25 degrees from the perpendicular to its orbital plane. Thus, Mars has seasonal changes much like the earth's, except they are slower, since the Martian year is six hundred eighty-seven of our days. Because of the eccentricity of Mars' orbit, the Southern Hemisphere receives about 50 per cent more intense sunlight during its summer than the Northern Hemisphere receives during its summer. White polar caps can be seen on the planet, perhaps formed of something similar to white frost, and these grow and shrink with the Martian seasons. Because of the greater extremes of temperature in the Southern Hemisphere, the south polar cap disappears entirely during the middle of its summer.

For more than two centuries, telescopes have been good enough to show a considerable amount of detail on the surface of Mars. The planet has a general orange or reddish color, broken up by large dark areas called maria. These are generally grayish, but take on a greenish tinge in what would be their spring season. The absence of strong infrared reflection shows the absence of appreciable amounts of chlorophyll, and thus the maria cannot be interpreted as being covered with higher order plants; however, recent studies of the infrared spectrum show characteristics in the maria, but not in other areas, which strongly resemble the laboratory spectra of materials which have a carbon-hydrogen bond, a chemical structure common in living materials. This suggests the possibility that the maria might be regions of some low form of vegetation, perhaps comparable to the lichens found on the earth.

Many years ago one group of good observers felt confident they could see a network of fine lines, or canals, which changed seasonally, but reappeared regularly in the same places with the recurrence of the same season. Another group of equally experienced observers using as good or better telescopes, reported disconnected dark patches but nothing that could be interpreted as the canals reported by the first group. Under absolutely perfect conditions, our largest telescopes should be just able to separate two points on Mars that are 4 miles apart. Due to problems inherent in our own atmosphere, the best resolution actually obtainable is probably more like 30 to 50 miles. Obviously, a canal would be too narrow to be seen, though irrigated areas of vegetation bordering a canal might possibly be detectable. Modern observations show that there is little water on Mars and make it extremely improbable that anything resembling canals could exist there. Yet, it is largely on the assumption that these markings were the result of artificially constructed canals that the claim for a highly developed civilization on Mars was made. Today, few, if any qualified astronomers, would argue that there is intelligent life there.

Mars definitely has an atmosphere, though it is much lower in density than the earth's. Red or infrared photographs are much clearer than those taken in blue light, showing that there is atmospheric scattering of the shorter wavelengths. A twilight zone is clearly observable. From time to time, detail is lost in small areas of the planet, indicating the existence of clouds or perhaps dust storms. A violet haze is observed to surround the planet, tentatively explained as a form of air glow in the upper Martian atmosphere.

Prior to July 14, 1965, when our Mariner IV passed within 6118 miles of Mars, it was believed that the Martian atmosphere might be 1/10 as dense as ours. The results of that probe indicate that the density is less than one per cent of the earth's sea-level atmospheric density, making it similar to our air at 100,000 feet above sea level. Fairly large amounts of carbon dioxide are found spectroscopically, the amount of water vapor is at most only a small fraction of that found in the earth's atmosphere, and the oxygen content appears to be much less than one per cent as great as we enjoy. Nitrogen, undetectable spectroscopically from the earth, is probably the commonest constituent of the Martian atmosphere, as it is in ours.

Photographs taken by Mariner IV show the surface of the planet to be covered with thousands of craters as large as 75 miles in diameter and 2 miles deep. They seem to be very rugged, resembling the mountains on the moon, and suggest that the surface of Mars has never been subjected to much erosion, or weathering. No magnetic field was detectable, and this fact, coupled with a mean density of less than four times the density of water, suggests that Mars may not have a heavy iron core similar to the earth's. In many ways, Mars resembles the moon much more than it resembles our planet.

During the 1877 favorable opposition of Mars, Asaph Hall at the United States Naval Observatory discovered two small satellites of Mars, and named them Phobos and Deimos, Fear and Panic, fit companions for

Figure 5.3. Mars photographed with the 36-inch Lick Refractor. Lick Observatory photograph.

Figure 5.4. A portion of the surface of Mars 170 miles wide photographed from a distance of 7800 miles on July 14, 1965, by Mariner IV. The similarity to portions of the moon's surface is striking. NASA photograph.

Mars, the God of War. Phobos, about 10 miles in diameter, revolves about Mars with a period of 7 hours 39 minutes and is only 3700 miles above the Martian surface. It is the only known natural satellite in the solar system which has a period of revolution shorter than the period of rotation of its primary. As seen from a point on Mars, Phobos would rise in the west and set in the east every 11 hours and 6 minutes.

Deimos, approximately 5 miles in diameter, revolves about Mars with a period of 30.3 hours at an average height of 12,100 miles above the planet's surface. Though it rises in the east and sets in the west, its period is so nearly equal to the rotation period of Mars that it is more than five Martian days between successive risings of Deimos. Between the time it rises and the time it sets, about sixty-five hours of our time later, Deimos goes through its full cycle of phases more than twice.

These two satellites of Mars are involved in one of the most remarkable fiction-science coincidences of all times. In 1726, more than a century and a half hour before Phobos and Deimos were discovered, Jonathan Swift wrote that the astronomers of Laputa had told Gulliver about two satellites of Mars "whereof the innermost is distant from the planet exactly three of his diameters, and the outermost five; the former revolves in a space of ten hours and the latter in twenty-one and a half." Swift could not possibly have known of the satellites, but even though his periods would have required both satellites to rise in the west and set in the east, his description was so close to the actual situation that for a time after Hall's discovery of the two satellites many people were unwilling to accept Swift's description as a mere coincidence.

The Asteroids. In 1772, J. E. Bode, the director of the Berlin Observatory, publicized an interesting series of numbers which had been discovered in 1766 by J. D. Titius of Wittenberg. Write down the series of numbers 0, 3, 6, 12, 24, etc. doubling the number each time after the first two. Then add 4 to each number and divide by ten. The result is a close approximation to the distance in astronomical units of each of the planets, Mercury through Uranus, from the sun. Uranus was not known in 1772, but when it was discovered in 1781, its measured distance agreed closely with the Bode-Titius prediction. There was, however, one point of apparent inaccuracy. The so-called law predicted a planet at a distance of 2.8 A.U. from the sun, and no planet was known between Mars at 1.52 A.U. and Jupiter at 5.2 A.U.

On the evening of January 1, 1801, the first night of the nineteenth century, a Sicilian astronomer, Giuseppe Piazzi (1746-1826), noticed a small starlike object which moved slowly with respect to the stars he was mapping in the region of Taurus. After six weeks of observing, Piazzi became ill, and before he could return to his telescope the object got too close to the sun for observation. The now-famous mathematician, C. F. Gauss, (1777-1855), who was then only twenty-four years old, devised a new method for computing the orbit of an object and predicted the future position of Piazzi's discovery. The tiny planet was relocated on the last night of the year of its discovery and was named Ceres.

Ceres' distance of 2.77 A.U. from the sun was in good agreement with the Bode-Titius prediction of 2.8 A.U., but its diameter of only 480 miles gave it a volume barely over 1/3 of one per cent of the volume of the smallest known planet, Mercury. The question of whether or not Ceres should be considered to be the missing planet was in some measure resolved by the discovery of three more asteroids: Pallas, with a diameter of 300 miles in 1802, Juno, 240 miles in diameter, found in 1804, and Vesta, only 120 miles in diameter, in 1807. By 1891, when photography was first used to search for asteroids, three hundred twenty-two had been discovered visually. Astronomical cameras revealed them in such vast numbers that in addition to about 2000 whose orbits have been computed, several thousand more must have been observed at least once. There are probably many tens of thousands that are within reach of our larger telescopes.

The first four asteroids, discovered more than a century and a half ago, are among the largest known, and altogether probably not more than twenty are over 100 miles in diameter. As we move to smaller and fainter asteroids, the number of individuals increases rapidly. Those under 1 mile in diameter are very likely to escape detection, though there may be hundreds of thousands of them. The lower limit of their size is unknown. Perhaps the particles that form the zodiacal light and many of the tens of millions of meteors which strike our atmosphere each day could be considered tiny asteroids much less than an inch in diameter. This possible connection will be considered again in Chapter 6.

In spite of the large number of individuals, the total mass of the asteroids is probably less than 1/1000 the mass of the earth. One asteroid 100 miles in diameter has a volume equal to 1 million asteroids 1 mile in diameter, or over 250 million, million, million particles 1 inch in diameter. Thus, even vast numbers of small asteroids would not produce a startling change in our estimates of the combined masses of the entire group.

The origin of the belt of asteroids is certainly not understood. If this is simply material that never formed into a planet, we are left with the question of why there is so little of it in this zone. Many of the meteorites (Chapter 6) show crystalline structures which suggest that they might be fragments of larger masses which solidified slowly under conditions of high temperature and pressure. If there were once a planet located between the orbits of Mars and Jupiter which blew up and scattered its debris around, we are left with the same question. Why is there so little material remaining in this region?

Because they are so small and starlike in appearance, the position of asteroids can be measured very accurately, permitting their orbits to be calculated with a high degree of precision. Though most of them revolve in the space between Mars and Jupiter, several pass quite close to the earth and prior to 1961 provided the best method known for determining the length of the Astronomical Unit in miles. From the elements of an asteroid's orbit, it is possible to calculate its precise distance from the earth in Astronomical Units at any given instant. For example, Eros passed within 0.1723 a.u. of the earth in 1931. At this time, its distance was also measured directly by triangulation from two stations on the earth and was found to be about 16 million miles. Thus, if 0.1723 a.u. equals 16 million miles, 1 a.u. would equal 16 million ÷ 0.1723, or 92,860,000 miles. The asteroid method for measuring the length of an Astronomical Unit was the most accurate known until 1961 when a radar measurement of the distance to Venus led to the currently accepted value of 92,960,000 miles.

Jupiter is 5.2 times the earth's distance from the sun and has a diameter that is eleven times as large as the earth's. Its volume is 50 per cent greater than all the other planets. It has about 1/10 the diameter, 1/1000 the volume and 1/1000 the mass of the sun. Jupiter is clearly the dominating planet in the solar system.

Seen through even a rather small telescope, Jupiter shows a disc crossed by alternating light and dark bands, tentatively explained as regions of rising and settling atmospheric gases. Details in the bands enable us to determine that the period of rotation of Jupiter is the shortest of any of the planets, 9 hours 55 minutes for most of the surface, though the equatorial regions seem to complete one rotation in 9 hours 50 minutes. Since we are observing the top of the Jovian atmosphere, some variation in speed is to be expected. The high rotational velocity, almost 8 miles per second at the equator, is sufficient to cause a noticeable bulge, so that the equatorial diameter is about seven per cent greater than the polar.

A large red spot, sometimes as much as 30,000 miles long, has been observed on Jupiter for almost a century and a half. Though it has undergone some changes in size, shape and color and has appeared to shift its position slightly, it definitely gives the impression of being a relatively permanent marking, anchored loosely to a fixed location. Various explanations, such as gases escaping from a fissure or a floating island of liquid or solid particles have been suggested, but the true nature of the great red spot still remains a mystery.

At Jupiter's distance from the sun it receives solar radiation less than 4 per cent as strong as that received by the earth. Thus, the measured temperature of −220°F at the visible cloud surface seems quite reasonable. Methane and ammonia have been definitely identified spectroscopically, and molecular hydrogen has been tentatively identified. The combination of low temperature and a surface gravity 2.64 times as great as the earth's, makes it almost certain that Jupiter has been able to retain large quantities of the lighter gases like hydrogen and helium.

It was formerly believed that Jupiter might have a solid, rocky core similar to that of the earth's, but it now seems more likely that the giant planet is composed almost entirely of hydrogen and helium, with only a relatively small percentage of the heavier elements. Because of the high gravitational attraction, pressures would increase very rapidly with a decrease in elevation. Only a few hundred miles below the top of the cloud layers the pressures would be great enough to liquify hydrogen and at a depth of a few hundred miles more, the liquid hydrogen would become solidified into something resembling ice. The central pressure has been calculated to be approximately three quarters of a million tons per square inch, and the density of the gases approximately four times the density of iron.

The fact that the central pressure of Jupiter is close to a critical value, means that Jupiter is about as large as a planet composed largely of hydrogen can be. If Jupiter had less mass it would be smaller than its present size. If it had much more mass, the central pressures would be above the critical value and electrons would be stripped from their atomic nuclei, making possible an even greater compression of material and resulting in a planet smaller than the present size of Jupiter.

Within the past ten years, long wave radiation in the radio range has been observed to be much stronger than would be expected considering the temperature of Jupiter. Not only is it polarized, but it seems to come from a region several times as large as the visible planet. It may originate from a zone of charged particles moving in a magnetic field surrounding the planet similar to the Van Allen belts which surround the earth.

Jupiter has a most interesting family of a dozen satellites. Except for the four largest, Io, Europa, Ganymede and Callisto, discovered by Galileo, they are unnamed and simply identified by a Roman numeral indicating the order of their discovery. The four Galilean satellites and a fifth, discovered by E. E. Barnard in 1892, range in distance from

113,000 to 1,169,000 miles from Jupiter. Their orbits are almost circular and are inclined only about 3 degrees to the plane of Jupiter's orbit. They all have direct motion, moving counterclockwise as seen from the north. The next three satellites, VI, VII and X, are all found between 7,100,000 and 7,300,000 miles from Jupiter, their orbits are moderately eccentric and inclined about 28 degrees to the plane of Jupiter's orbit, and their motion, too, is direct. The last four, XII, XI, VIII and IX, are found between 13 and 15 million miles from Jupiter; their orbits are quite eccentric and inclined at various angles, and they all have retrograde motion. Io and Europa are about the size of our moon; Ganymede and Callisto are about the size of Mercury. All the rest are probably less than 100 miles in diameter, and numbers VIII through XII are estimated to be only about 15 miles in diameter. The characteristics of these satellites will be considered again in Chapter 7 in connection with the formation of the solar system.

Saturn is the most spectacular of the planets. It is 72,000 miles in diameter and has a mass ninety-five times as great as the earth's.

Figure 5.5 Jupiter photographed with the 36-inch Lick Refractor. Lick Observatory photograph.

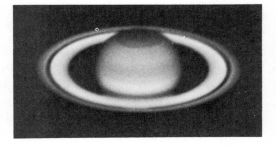

Figure 5.6. Saturn photographed with the 36-inch Lick Refractor. Lick Observatory photograph.

Though its volume is roughly 3/5 that of Jupiter, its mass is only about 1/3 as great. Thus, the average density of Saturn is only about 0.71 that of water. If, as seems likely, its composition is similar to Jupiter's, largely hydrogen and helium, the low density is not hard to understand. Its smaller mass would exert less gravitational pull, and the gases would not be nearly as highly compressed. Theoretical calculations give Saturn only about 1/2 the central pressure and density of Jupiter.

Saturn is about ten times the earth's distance from the sun, so the solar radiation it receives is about one per cent as intense as ours. Its temperature is about −230°F. Both methane and ammonia have been identified in Saturn's atmosphere, but its ammonia spectrum is weaker than Jupiter's, probably because the lower temperature of Saturn has frozen out much of it. Cloud belts can be seen, but they are less clearly defined than those of Jupiter. Saturn's period of rotation is 10 hours 38 minutes, slightly longer than Jupiter's. We will see later that this is exactly what would be expected as a result of a lower degree of contraction and a greater distance from the sun.

Saturn's most spectacular characteristic is its system of three, flat concentric rings lying in the planet's equatorial plane. Though they were first seen by Galileo, it required better telescopes than he had to determine their true nature. The inner, or crape ring begins about 7000 miles above the visible surface of Saturn and extends outward for 11,000 miles. After a gap of about a thousand miles the middle and brightest ring begins and extends outward for another 15,000 miles. Outside this, there is a gap of 2500 miles, called Cassenni's division, before the outer ring begins its 10,000 mile extension. The overall diameter of the outer ring is 171,000 miles, almost 3/4 as great as the distance from the earth to the moon.

Saturn circles the sun once each 29.5 years, and its equatorial plane is inclined about 28 degrees to the plane of its orbit. At least twice during each 29.5 year period, the earth passes through the plane of the rings, and at this time the rings completely disappear, indicating that they are probably not more than 10 miles thick. If a scale model of Saturn were made with the planet two feet in diameter, the rings would have a diameter of 4 feet 9 inches, and a thickness about equal to the thickness of one page in this book. The spectrum of the rings shows they are small, solid particles reflecting sunlight, and that the inner parts move more rapidly than the outer parts in accordance with Kepler's laws. If they were a solid sheet of material the outside would move faster than the inside. Stars can be seen through the rings, proving again that they are composed of discrete particles.

Saturn has ten satellites, all but the tenth discovered, interestingly enough, before the end of the nineteenth century. They do not show the grouping that was prominent in Jupiter's satellites, and only one, the outermost, has retrograde motion. The largest, Titan, is 2600 miles in diameter, and with the discovery of methane in its spectrum became the only satellite in the solar system definitely known to have an atmosphere.

In 1850, E. A. Roche pointed out that if a satellite which had no tensile strength of its own were to come nearer than 2.44 times the radius of a planet from that planet's center, the satellite would be torn apart by the tidal forces and the material scattered around the planet in the form of a ring. The outer edge of the third ring is at a distance of about 2.4 radii from Saturn's center; Janus, the tenth satellite, which was discovered in December, 1966, while the rings were edgewise to the earth, is at a mean distance of 2.64 radii from the planet's center. Though it is possible that the three rings were formed by the tidal break up of three former satellites, it is also entirely possible they were formed from preplanetary material which was prevented from forming into satellites by the strong tidal forces.

Uranus is the first planet to have been discovered within historic times. In the latter part of the eighteenth century, William Herschel, (1738-1822), then a professional musician and amateur astronomer, undertook the formidable task of carefully examining every star that could be seen with his 7-inch homemade telescope. On the evening of March 13, 1781, he noted that one of the stars in Gemini seemed to have a tiny greenish disc, though stars normally appear to be mere pinpoints of light. A few nights of careful observing made it clear that this object was not a star, because it moved with respect to the other stars in the region. Herschel first suspected that it was a comet, but A. J. Lexell computed its orbit and identified the object as a planet circling the sun in an elliptical orbit every eighty-four years. Its mean distance of 19.182 A.U. from the sun was in close agreement with the Bode-Titius prediction of 19.6 A.U. Herschel first named his planet Georgium Sidus in honor of George III of England. The name, however, was not internationally acceptable, and for a time the new planet was called Herschel. About a century ago, the director of the Berlin Observatory, J. E. Bode, suggested the name Uranus, who was the mythical God of the Heavens.

Under favorable conditions Uranus can be faintly seen with the naked eye, but with a diameter of only about 30,000 miles, about four times the diameter of the earth and a minimum distance from the earth of about 1 2/3 billion miles, the maximum angular diameter of the planet is less than 4 seconds of arc. This makes the planet look about the same size as a Ping-pong ball seen at a distance of 2 miles. The observation of fine detail is thus difficult. Its mass, determined from the periods and distances of its satellites, is about 14.6 times the mass of the earth, giving the planet an average density about one and one-half times the density of water. It seems quite likely that Uranus is composed of highly compressed gases, similar to the structure suggested for Jupiter and Saturn. If this is the correct explanation, the much smaller mass coupled with the rather high mean density would imply a somewhat lower percentage of hydrogen than is found in the two giant planets.

At its mean distance of almost 20 A.U. from the sun, the radiation received by Uranus is only about 1/4 of one per cent as strong as that received by the earth. The resulting surface temperature is below −300°F. The spectrum shows methane, but no ammonia, probably because it has all been frozen out at the low temperature. A series of infra-red absorption lines in the spectrum of Uranus was identified in 1952 by G. P. Kuiper and G. Herzberg as being produced by molecular hydrogen. This was the first identification of hydrogen in the spectra of any of the planets.

Uranus' period of revolution around the sun is eighty-four years, and it rotates on its axis every 10.7 hours. The nature of its rotation is, however, unique among the planets. Typically, the axes of the planets are nearly perpendicular to the planes of their orbits, and in most cases the direction of rotation of the planet is counterclockwise as seen from the north. With Uranus, however, its axis lies within 8 degrees of the plane of its orbit, and the rotation of the planet as seen from its north pole is clockwise. Thus, in the course of one Uranian year the sun would at some time shine perpendicularly on every part of the planet between latitudes 82 degrees south and 82 degrees north. Each pole would enjoy a long day, equal in length to forty-two of our years, and during the middle of this day, the sun would be only 8 degrees away from the zenith. It would then be more nearly directly overhead than it ever gets at any point on the earth that is south of Cordoba, Argentina or north of Tucson, Arizona. If Uranus were not so far from the sun, this would lead to extreme seasonal variations in temperature.

Uranus has five satellites, none as large as our moon, and they all move in orbits that are in the plane of Uranus' equator. In 1966, their orbits were exactly edgewise to the earth, so the apparent motions of the satellites were up and down along a straight line. In 1987, the orbits will be seen flat in the sky, so the satellites will appear to move in almost circular orbits.

Neptune was discovered in 1846, and its discovery is considered to be one of the great triumphs of mathematical astronomy. After the calculation of the orbit of Uranus, its future positions were predicted, but Uranus failed to follow the predictions. Revised calculations still failed to account for the motions accurately enough to satisfy astronomers. A person with good eyesight can just separate two stars that are 3 minutes of arc apart. The difference between the observed and predicted positions of Uranus reached the "intolerable" value of 2 minutes! So two mathematicians, John Couch Adams (1819-1892) in England and Urbain Leverrier (1811-1877) in France, working independently, set themselves the task of calculating where an hitherto unknown planet would have to be to produce the observed perturbations in the orbit of Uranus.

Adams completed his work and sent his predictions to the British Astronomer Royal. Astronomical photography was unknown at this time, but eventually a manuscript map was made at Cambridge of the region of the sky suspected of containing the unknown planet. The plan was to wait for a time so the hoped-for planet would move enough to reveal its identity.

While this was going on, Leverrier completed his calculations and sent the results to the Paris Observatory, but the figures were returned to Leverrier without a search having been made. Leverrier then wrote to a friend, Johann Galle, at the Berlin Observatory, saying, "Direct your telescope to a point on the ecliptic in the constellation Aquarius, in longitude 326°, and you will find within a degree of that place a new planet, looking like a star of about the ninth magnitude and having a perceptible disk." Galle began the search the same evening he received the letter and, aided by a map of the area which had been made earlier for another purpose, found the new planet within half an hour, and only 52 minutes of arc away from the predicted position. When the news of the discovery reached Cambridge, their map was brought out, and it was found that they had seen and plotted the planet, but had failed to recognize it.

The new planet, Neptune, was found to circle the sun in one hundred sixty-five years at a mean distance of about 30 A.U. This was quite different from the Bode-Titus prediction of 38.8 A.U. At this distance, it receives solar radiation only 1/9 of one per cent as strong as the earth, and its resulting temperature is about −350°F.

Neptune appears to be almost a carbon copy of Uranus. Its diameter of about 28,000 miles and mass seventeen times the earth's give it a density about twice that of water. Both methane and ammonia have been identified in its spectrum. Internally, it is probably much like Uranus, with a somewhat lower percentage of hydrogen than is found in Jupiter and Saturn.

Neptune rotates in about sixteen hours, so there are about 90,000 Neptunian days in a Neptunian year. Its axis is tilted only about 29 degrees away from the perpendicular to its orbital plane, in the same general range as most of the planets in the solar system.

Neptune has two known satellites. Triton is somewhat larger than our moon and has retrograde motion in an almost circular orbit with a period of just under six days. It probably has some atmosphere. Nereid is not more than a few hundred miles in diameter, has a period of revolution of almost a year, and has the most eccentric orbit of any known satellite. Its distance from Neptune varies all the way from just over 800,000 miles to just over 6 million.

Pluto was discovered in 1930 at the Lowell Observatory by Clyde Tombaugh. After Neptune had been observed for half a century its observed positions seemed to deviate slightly from its predicted positions, but the discrepancies in this case were of the same order of magnitude as the slight but unavoidable errors in measuring its position. In spite of the uncertain data, a number of astronomers tried to predict the position of a trans-Neptunian planet during the years around the beginning of the present century. Among them was Percival Lowell, who founded and endowed the Lowell Observatory at Flagstaff, Arizona. Although Lowell himself never was able to find the planet, Tombaugh was searching photographically in the predicted location when he found Pluto. The new planet was within 6 degrees of the predicted position, but subsequent investigations make it doubtful that Pluto has mass enough to produce the supposed perturbations on which Lowell based his calculations. Regardless of whether or not this should be considered a predicted discovery, the fact remains that Pluto was found as a direct consequence of Lowell's calculations.

Both the diameter and the mass of Pluto are still somewhat uncertain, but both are almost certainly smaller than the earth's. It circles the sun once every 248.4 years at an average distance of 39.5 A.U., though its orbit is so eccentric that its distance from the sun may be as little as 29.6 A.U. or as much as 49.4 A.U. At perihelion Pluto is 63 million miles nearer the sun than Neptune, but Pluto's orbit is so highly inclined, about 17 degrees to the plane of the ecliptic, that there is no chance of a collision between the two planets.

Pluto's small size and eccentric orbit have raised the question of whether it might not be an escaped satellite of Neptune. The answer may not be known definitely until we understand more about Pluto itself and more about how the planets were formed. Regardless of its past history, however, at the present time Pluto is as much a planet as any of the other members of the sun's family.

TABLE 1 SOME CHARACTERISTICS OF THE PLANETS AND THEIR ORBITS

| Body | Mean distance from the sun | | Period of revolution in days | | Eccentricity of Orbit | Mean Diameter miles | Mass, Earth = 1 | Density, water = 1 | Sidereal period of rotation, days | Brightest apparent magnitude |
	A.U.	Million miles	Sidereal	Synodic						
Sun						865,400	335,000	1.4	25 to 34d	-26.7
Moon		(238,857)	(27.322)	(29.531)	(0.055)	2,159	0.0123	3.33	27.322d	-12.5
Mercury	0.387	35.98	87.97	115.88	0.206	3,100	0.054	5.4	60d ±	- 1.9
Venus	0.723	67.24	224.70	583.92	0.007	7,700	0.815	5.1	247d*	- 4.4
Earth	1.000	92.96	365.26	------	0.017	7,918	1.000	5.52	23h 56m	---
Mars	1.524	141.63	686.98	779.94	0.093	4,150	0.108	3.97	24h 37m	- 2.8
Ceres	2.767	257.37	4.69y	466.6	0.076	434	0.0001	4.2	9h 05m	+ 4.0
Jupiter	5.203	483.6	11.86y	398.88	0.048	86,700	317.8	1.33	9h 50m	- 2.5
Saturn	9.540	886.7	29.46y	378.09	0.056	72,300	95.2	0.68	10h 14m	- 0.4
Uranus	19.18	1782.7	84.01y	369.66	0.047	29,500	14.5	1.60	10h 49m	+ 5.6
Neptune	30.07	2795.0	164.79y	367.49	0.009	27,800	17.2	2.25	15h ?	+ 7.9
Pluto	39.44	3666.1	248.43y	366.74	0.249	4,000?	?	?	6d 09h	+14.9

The values for the moon which are enclosed in parenthesis refer to its orbit around the earth.

*The rotation of Venus appears to be in a clockwise direction as seen from the north.

SUMMARY

In the sun's planetary family there is obviously a wide range in size, mass, constitution, temperature, atmosphere and satellite systems. During the past centuries these characteristics have been of purely scientific interest. During the next decade they may become of prime importance as they describe the environment in which exploring parties from the earth will be working.

We cannot even wonder intelligently about the origin of the earth without wondering about the origin of the other planets in the solar system. Many billions of years ago there must have been a comparatively orderly development which resulted in the diversification which we observe today. In Chapter 7 we will return to some of the thinking along these lines.

CHAPTER

6

The Comets
and Meteors

TOPICS

Cometary orbits

The source of comets

The physical nature of comets

Composition of a comet

Meteors

Meteor craters

Meteorites

Meteor showers

The zodiacal light and counterglow

The source of interplanetary material

On any good clear moonless night, an observer who is well away from streetlights and the bright sky of a city should be able to see perhaps half a dozen shooting stars per hour. They are properly called meteors and will be considered later in this chapter. Comets are a much more uncommon phenomenon. Although ten or a dozen may be observed each year photographically, it may be several years between the appearance of comets bright enough to be noticeable with the naked eye, and there are perhaps a dozen or less really spectacular comets each century. Most of those that can be seen without telescopic aid look like a faint, misty spot somewhat smaller than the full moon, which moves so slowly with respect to the stellar background that they appear to be stationary. From one night to the next, however, a naked-eye comet will usually move quite a few degrees, so it may appear in a different constellation on successive evenings.

Prior to 1700, comets were generally feared and were superstitiously considered to be omens of disaster. After the publication of Newton's law of gravitation in 1687, Sir Edmund Halley (1656-1722) computed the orbits of a number of comets for which good observations were available, publishing his calculations for two dozen of them in 1705. He noted that very bright comets had been seen in 1456, 1531, 1607 and 1682 at intervals of seventy-five or seventy-six years. He further noted that the elements of the orbits of these four comets were very similar and concluded that what had been assumed to be four different comets were, in fact, the same comet, moving in an elongated orbit which brought it close to the sun every three-quarters of a century. Halley predicted that it would be seen again late in 1758 or early in 1759, and though he died in 1722, the comet which now bears his name was rediscovered on Christmas night, 1758. Over the centuries, the orbit of Halley's comet has been altered slightly many times by the gravitational attraction of

Figure 6.1. The head of Halley's comet, photographed May 8, 1910, with the 60-inch reflector on Mount Wilson. Photograph from the Mount Wilson and Palomar Observatories.

the larger planets, particularly Jupiter, so that the period of revolution about the sun has varied between seventy-four and seventy-nine years. A search of early records, both oriental and occidental, has revealed at least a brief mention of this comet at every return since 240 B.C. The last perihelion passage of Halley's comet was in 1910, and it will again come close to the sun in 1986.

COMETARY ORBITS

Any body which in moving under the gravitational control of the sun must travel in an orbit which is either an ellipse, a parabola or an hyperbola. An ellipse may have a variety of shapes. It may be almost circular or it may be extremely elongated. Any body moving on an elliptical orbit will cover the same path again and again, swinging around the sun at regular intervals. It would thus be a permanent member of the solar system.

Parabolas and hyperbolas are open curves, and an object moving on either of these orbits would approach the sun only once and would therefore not be a permanent member of the sun's family. Any body

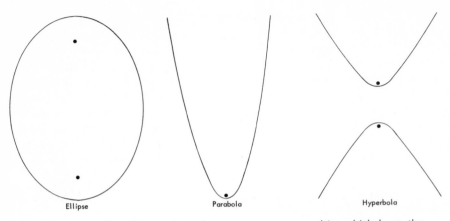

Ellipse   Parabola   Hyperbola

Figure 6.2. All bodies in the solar system move on orbits which have the shape of one of the conic sections.

approaching the sun from interstellar space would have an hyperbolic orbit.

THE SOURCE OF COMETS

Many astronomers believe that a hundred billion or more comets may exist at distances between 50,000 and 150,000 A.U. from the sun where their periods of revolution about the sun would lie between four million and sixty million years. The attraction of the nearer stars might alter some of the orbits so that from time to time a comet could escape from the sun's gravitational hold and wander off into interstellar space. Others might be turned in so they would pass through the planetary system and perhaps be visible from the earth. The small section of one of these long elliptical orbits near the sun where a comet can be observed is indistinguishable from a parabolic orbit. Comets on near-parabolic orbits seem to come in about equal numbers from all parts of the sky.

If one of these comets happens to pass near a planet the shape of its orbit will again be changed. If it is made hyperbolic the comet will escape entirely from the solar system. If it is made less eccentric, the comet will remain nearer the sun and orbit in a much shorter time. Each time it happens to pass near a planet it will suffer additional perturbations. The chance of repeated perturbations is increased if the orbit is not too highly inclined to the planets' orbits and if it is moving in the same direction as the planets revolve. The orbits of the majority of the comets having periods of under a hundred years show these characteristics. The orbits of between forty and fifty comets reach their most distant point from the sun near the orbit of Jupiter. These comets are known as Jupiter's family. Smaller but similar families are probably associated with the other large planets.

If comets were not members of our solar system but entered it from interstellar space, they should move on hyperbolic orbits. No comet has ever been observed which approached the sun on a clearly hyperbolic orbit. We must therefore conclude that comets are members of the solar system.

THE PHYSICAL NATURE OF COMETS

Comets are known to have very little mass. Though their orbits are noticeably changed when they pass close to a major planet, the planet itself is unaffected. In 1886, Comet Brooks II passed through Jupiter's satellite system without altering the periods of any of the individual satellites by a measurable amount. In 1770 Lexell's comet passed close to the earth but produced no detectable change in the earth's motions. If the mass of either of these comets had been as much as 1/100,000 the earth's mass, a measurable change would have been detected. Based on the amount of light comets reflect, several investigators agree that the mass of a comet may be as little as a millionth of a millionth of the earth's mass. Oort has estimated that the total mass of perhaps a hundred billion comets in the comet reservoir is probably only between 1/10 and 1/100 that of the earth.

The Composition of a Comet

Many comets are observed to have a small, bright nucleus which is surrounded by a much larger, fainter, almost spherical coma. As the comet approaches the sun it may develop a long tail which invariably points away from the sun.

According to Whipple's Dirty Ice theory, the nucleus of a comet when it is quite distant from the sun is composed of a loose mass of frozen gases from a few miles to a few hundred miles in diameter in which are imbedded large numbers of small, rocky or metallic particles. At distances comparable to those of the outer planets and beyond, the comet must have a temperature close to absolute zero and would reflect so little sunlight that it would be invisible in even our large telescopes.

When comets are observed at distances approximating 5 A.U. from the sun, their spectra show they are merely reflecting sunlight, indicating that at this distance the comet is largely composed of particles of solid material. As the comet approaches the sun it receives increasing amounts of energy, and gases are ejected in all directions from the nucleus, forming a more or less spherical coma that is frequently between 50,000 and 100,000 miles in diameter. As the comet continues to approach the sun it develops a bright line, or emission spectrum, showing the presence of gases made up of various compounds of hydrogen, carbon, nitrogen and oxygen. These radicals are presumably released by the photodissociation of the ices in the nucleus.

Many, but not all comets, develop a tail as they approach the sun. The material which is ejected from the nucleus in all directions is forced back away from the sun by the radiation pressure of the sunlight. Each individual particle is also under the gravitational influence of the sun, so it is in orbit and tends to move more slowly as its distance from the sun increases. Thus, the tail always points away from the sun but curves slightly, lagging behind the motion of the head. The gravitational attraction depends on the mass of the individual particle, and the repulsive force of the radiation pressure depends on its cross section. For large pieces of material the radiation pressure is relatively insignificant in comparison to the gravitational attraction, but for particles approaching molecular size the radiation pressure is the larger of the two. Some comets have developed several tails fanning out away from the sun. These may be composed of different sized particles for which the relative strengths of the attractive and repulsive forces would be dissimilar.

With the possible exception of the sun's corona, the tails of comets are the largest things in the solar system. Several have been known to reach a length of 100 million miles. Yet the amount of material, the mass, involved in the tail of a comet is extremely small. It has been calculated that one ounce of comet tail would cover the entire United States to the depth of half a mile.

Comets usually become much brighter as they approach the sun and dimmer as they recede, but occasionally they show sudden, rather large changes in brightness for which no clear explanation is immediately available. Some of the variations may result from fluctuations in high-energy radiation from the sun, and some may come from readjustment of the material in the nucleus of the comet which would expose clean and volatile surfaces to the solar radiation.

Comets which repeatedly pass close to the sun cannot be expected to last forever. On each trip they must lose some fraction of the frozen material, and after perhaps a hundred near approaches the ices may become completely evaporated, leaving only a swarm of meteoric particles to orbit in the path of the former comet.

In 1668, 1843, 1880, 1882 and 1887, brilliant comets were seen which were all traveling on nearly identical paths that passed within 300,000 miles of the sun. Their individual periods ranged up to many centuries so they could not possibly have been the same comet on successive perihelion passages. One of them, the Great Comet of 1882, was so brilliant that it could be seen in the daytime. It approached the sun as a single comet, but it broke into four separate comets as it passed perihelion. These four then moved away on slightly different orbits which will bring them back at intervals of roughly a hundred years between the twenty-fifth and twenty-ninth centuries. The five individuals which constituted the original comet group probably resulted from a similar tidal break-up of a single large prehistoric comet.

METEORS

Meteors, or shooting stars, are of more frequent occurrence than most people realize. Careful counts, prorated from the area that a single observer can cover, indicate that approximately a million meteors bright enough to be seen with the naked eye enter the earth's atmosphere each hour. The number bright enough to be seen with binoculars must run into several billion each day. Because each meteoric particle is so small, the total mass added to the earth probably does not exceed a few tons per day, relatively insignificant in comparison with the earth's mass of 6,600 million million million tons.

Meteoroids are small particles of solid material that are orbiting the sun in interplanetary space. When one is close enough to the earth to be drawn into our atmosphere, usually with a speed between 8 and 45 miles per second, it is heated to incandescence and can then be seen as a meteor. If it is large enough to survive its trip through the atmosphere and land on the surface of the earth, it is called a meteorite.

Most meteors, even relatively bright ones, are produced by surprisingly small meteoroids weighing something like 1/100 ounce and having a size not many times larger than the head of a pin. They come into our outer atmosphere with speeds of several tens of miles per second (the bullet from a high-powered rifle has a muzzle velocity of only a little over half a mile a second) and by the time they have penetrated to a height of 60 to 80 miles above the earth's surface, the friction with our air has heated them to incandescence. The spectra of a few meteors have been photographed, and these usually show bright emission lines of calcium and iron and indicate a temperature of several thousand degrees. If all the light came from a glowing solid it would have a continuous spectrum. Thus, much of the light must come from luminous gases driven out of the meteoroid by the intense heat. Occasionally, an extremely bright meteor will leave a luminous train which remains visible for several minutes or longer. Most meteors have completely disintegrated and disappeared by the time they are fifty miles above the earth's surface.

Quite infrequently, one may see a meteor that is more brilliant than the brightest stars and planets or even rivals the full moon. When such an object is bright enough to cast visible shadows it is called a fireball. Because it is so extremely luminous, it gives the impression of being a large object, but the meteoroid which produces it is rarely larger than a basketball.

If a large meteoroid strikes our atmosphere almost tangentially, so it has a long path through the air, it may become intensely heated on the outside while the central parts remain extremely cold. The strains set up can cause the meteoroid to shatter or explode. Such a bursting meteor is called a bolide, and in a few cases the sound of an explosion has been reported. In a number of instances many fragments totaling several hundred pounds have been found on the earth's surface, with the smaller pieces dropping nearer to the point of explosion and the larger chunks carrying on to a considerably greater distance. It is also possible that a compact swarm of sizable meteoroids may enter our atmosphere, and in either case, the large number of meteorites falling to the earth almost simultaneously within a limited area is known as a meteor fall.

METEOR CRATERS

Very rarely, perhaps on the average only once in several centuries, a meteoroid which weighs hundreds or thousands of tons may strike the earth, producing a clearly defined crater. The largest of these which has been positively identified is the Barringer crater near Winslow, Arizona. It is about four-fifths a mile across, the 60-acre floor is about 600 feet below the rim, and the rim stands 150 feet above the surrounding plain. Repeated borings have failed to locate any large meteoric mass, but they do show that the material under the crater is pulverized and that the rock strata are tilted upward all around the crater. Large numbers of pieces of meteoric iron have been found in the area, ranging in size from tiny fragments weighing a fraction of an ounce to large chunks weighing several hundred pounds. The dry climate has preserved the crater a long time, but its exact age is uncertain, with estimates ranging from as little as five thousand years to as many as seventy-five thousand.

The crater was probably formed by a large iron meteoroid weighing perhaps hundreds of thousands of tons which struck the earth with a speed of several tens of miles per second, penetrating the earth's crust for at most a few thousand feet. Its tremendous kinetic energy was converted into heat within a small fraction of a second, producing a

Figure 6.3. The Barringer meteor crater near Winslow, Arizona. Yerkes Observatory photograph.

violent subterranean explosion which blew out the crater, pulverized the rock strata and scattered fragments throughout the surrounding area.

Throughout the world several dozen craters are recognized as being certainly or probably of metoric origin. Many more must have been destroyed by erosion or concealed by vegetation, and at least three quarters of all large meteoric masses must have landed in an ocean where no crater would be formed.

METEORITES

Over the past centuries, a large but unknown number of meteoroids have survived their trip through our atmosphere and reached the surface of the earth as solid pieces of material. They are called meteorites, and

Figure 6.4. Section of an iron meteorite showing the crystalline structure. Yerkes Observatory photograph.

hundreds of pieces have been found, the smallest weighing only a fraction of an ounce and the largest thus far identified being the 50-ton Hoba West meteorite found near Grootfontein, South-West Africa.

There are three major kinds of meteorites: the irons, or siderites, composed mostly of iron but usually containing significant amounts of nickel; the comparatively rare stony irons, or siderolites, composed of nodules of stone imbedded in a matrix of iron; the stones, or aerolites, made of stony material with only small amounts of iron. Though the stony meteors are probably the most common, they are so similar to terrestrial rocks that they are likely to escape detection. All meteorites show a fused outer surface, resulting from the intense heating during their trip through the atmosphere. When an iron meteorite is sectioned and the cut surface polished and then etched with acid, a characteristic crystalline structure, known as the Widmunstätten figures, appears. The etched surface seems to be covered with long, needle-like crystals interlaced to form a triangular or hexagonal pattern and provides positive identification of the mass as being meteoritic.

The structure of meteorites may hold important clues relative to the formation of the entire solar system, but as yet the interpretation is not clear. Many of the stony meteorites appear to have formed as parts of a much larger mass. The crystalline structure of the iron meteors would seem to indicate that they had cooled gradually from a molten condition, but when or where they formed and how they came to be floating around in interplanetary space is still an unanswered question.

Many meteors must have the same structure as the meteorites which have been recovered. Evidence is accumulating, however, that some meteors are produced by small masses of frozen gases which shatter as the result of their high speed through the air and then evaporate completely, leaving no recoverable meteorite.

Meteor Showers

Not infrequently, we experience a meteor shower in which, for a period of several hours or even a few days, abnormally large numbers of meteors are observed. These meteoroids are actually moving as a swarm or stream in interplanetary space. When the earth's orbital motion carries it through such a swarm, the parallel paths of the meteors as they enter our atmosphere are seen in perspective and, like the parallel rails of a train track which seem to come from a single point on the horizon, the meteors appear to be moving away from some fixed point in the sky called the radiant.

The most spectacular shower on record occurred in 1833 when, according to observers, there were so many meteors that they looked like a heavy snowfall. Individual observers estimated that they were seeing 200,000 meteors an hour for five or six hours, all apparently radiating from a region in Leo. A similar spectacular shower occurred in 1866, and calculations showed that the main swarm was orbiting the sun about every thirty-three years. When no unusually large numbers of meteors were seen in 1899 or 1900 or again in 1932 or 1933, it was feared that the swarm might have become so dispersed that it would never again produce an outstanding display, but a recalculation of the orbit of the swarm by computer predicted that the 1966 Leonid shower might again be brilliant. Unfortunately, most of the United States was cloudy, but in a few regions in the southwest where the sky was clear the shower was very intense.

Figure 6.5. The November 1966, Leonid meteor shower, photographed by Mr. David R. McLean from the Kitt Peak National Observatory in Tucson, Arizona. Photograph courtesy of Mr. David R. McLean and the Lunar and Planetary Observatory of the University of Arizona.

Most meteor showers, however, are not spectacular. A watcher would simply see a few more meteors than on a normal night, and most of them would seem to be coming from one particular region of the sky.

The orbits of about a dozen shower-producing meteoroid swarms have been calculated and have been found to coincide with the orbits of known periodic comets, though some of the comets no longer appear. In some cases, the cometary debris seems to be strewn more or less uniformly around the orbit, so that we have meteor showers of approximately equal intensity each year when the earth passes through the meteoroid stream. In other cases, resulting perhaps from the more recent disintegration of a comet, a relatively compact swarm of meteoroids is orbiting the sun, and if the earth happens to pass directly through this swarm we may get a really spectacular shower.

THE ZODIACAL LIGHT AND COUNTERGLOW

In the western sky just after dark, or in the eastern sky just before dawn, it is frequently possible to see a diffuse cone of light tapering upward from the horizon along the ecliptic. This zodiacal light is most clearly seen in the evening in March and April and in the morning in September and October. At these times, the ecliptic (the apparent path of the sun which marks the center of the zodiacal belt) is most nearly perpendicular to the horizon in the Northern Hemisphere. In the tropics, one time of year is about as good as another. Under favorable conditions the zodiacal light may be seen to extend well over half way from the horizon to the zenith, and there is definite evidence to show that it actually circles the sky completely but is much brighter near the sun.

Figure 6.6. The zodiacal light produced the glow at the left side of this picture. The Milky Way from Cassiopeia to Canis Major crosses from top to bottom just to the right of the center. Yerkes Observatory photograph.

Directly opposite the sun the zodiacal light brightens appreciably in an area some 10 degrees long to produce the counterglow, or gegenschein. Though it is readily measurable with modern photometers and has been photographed repeatedly, it is so faint that most people are unable to see it visually.

The spectrum of the zodiacal light is that of reflected sunlight, indicating the presence of vast numbers of small particles of solid material distributed in a relatively thin, flat web surrounding the sun in the interplanetary regions. The particles close to the sun reflect more sunlight than those farther away, producing the conical appearance of the zodiacal light. Two possible explanations of the counterglow have been suggested. Particles directly opposite the sun may reflect more light than they do in other positions, a full moon effect, which could produce the observed brightening of the zodiacal light. It has also been shown that the gravitational effect of the earth combining with that of the sun would produce a region just under 1 million miles from the earth in a direction opposite to that of the sun in which particles would become trapped and have a revolution period of exactly one year. In this case, the counterglow would result from an actual increase in the number of particles per cubic mile. It may well turn out that the observed effect results from a combination of both of these causes.

THE SOURCE OF INTERPLANETARY MATERIAL

Within the past few decades it has become increasingly evident that interplanetary space, once thought to be relatively devoid of material, is actually fairly densely populated. Unfortunately, the mere recognition that this interplanetary debris exists does not explain where it came from.

Some of the questions raised by the asteroids were mentioned in Chapter 5. There are relatively few greater than 100 miles in diameter, but as we go down in size toward about a mile in diameter, the practical limit for present telescopic observation, the numbers increase into the thousands. Could there be millions of small asteroids a few feet or even a fraction of an inch in diameter? Could these be the source of meteoritic material? If they resulted from the break-up of larger bodies, either through collision or explosion, this might explain the internal structure of the meteorites which have been recovered. Vast numbers of these small particles, held gravitationally close to the common plane of the planetary orbits suggest an explanation of the zodiacal light, but even the most generous estimates of the total amount of material involved fall far short of reaching the mass of even a very modest planet.

The established connection between comets and meteor showers and the evidence that many meteors may be composed of frozen gases rather than iron or stone suggest that perhaps much of the interplanetary material might be of cometary origin. Even this, however, is not an entirely satisfactory answer. Comets may originate in a comet reservoir, but what produced the reservoir in the first place? And if comet nuclei are made up of dirty ice, how can we explain the source of the particles of solid material, stone or iron, which we think are imbedded in the frozen gases?

Perhaps we do not need to explain the origin of the zodiacal light particles and the smaller meteoroids on the basis of either comets or asteroids. It may well be that several billions of years ago when the

planets were forming out of a primordial cloud, some of the material
simply never got consolidated into planets but remained a thin dusty
web near the equatorial plane of the rotating mass. The sun shining on
such a web would produce our zodiacal light. Particles of its material
striking our atmosphere at high speed would produce the fainter meteors.
If only we could be more specific about the details of the formation of
the planetary system as a whole we would be in a better position to
explain the nature of its parts.

7

The Origin
of the Solar System

TOPICS

Laplace's nebular hypothesis   Dynamic encounter theories
The protoplanet hypothesis

THE PROBLEM

For thousands of years man has been trying to explain the origin of the universe, and even today no completely acceptable theory has been suggested. Before we look at three major proposals that have received rather general acceptance, let us examine the problem.

Any tenable theory must provide for a system of planets with a wide range of distance from a central sun and with their revolution essentially in the same plane and all in the same direction. Their axes of rotation must be, with one exception, roughly perpendicular to their orbital planes, and the theory should explain why the smaller planets near the sun have longer periods of rotation than the larger planets farther out. We would like at least a general explanation of the masses of the different planets, their densities, and if possible, an explanation of their chemical constitution insofar as it is known. We want to know why some planets have no atmosphere, some a comparatively thin one and still others a dense mantle of gas and clouds. We would like to know why the space between the orbits of Mars and Jupiter contains thousands of asteroids, rather than a single planet. We will want an explanation of why 98 per cent of the angular momentum of the entire system is vested in the planets, and only about 2 per cent in the sun, in spite of the fact that the sun is seven hundred forty-five times as massive as all of the planets combined. We would like to know why one planet has a dozen satellites and two, at least, have none; why some of these satellites have eccentric orbits while others are almost circular; why it is that although 4/5 the satellites revolve around their primaries in a counterclockwise direction as seen from the north, 1/5 go in the opposite direction.

We would like an explanation of the nature and origin of comets, meteors and the zodiacal light, the interrelation between them, and how they fit into the picture of the entire solar system.

The problem is a difficult one. It is not surprising that no complete explanation has yet been developed.

LAPLACE'S NEBULAR HYPOTHESIS

Around the middle of the eighteenth century, I. Kant speculated that the sun and planets might have evolved from some large rotating mass of gas and dust. P. S. Laplace expanded on the idea, and in 1796 published his Nebular Hypothesis, which dominated scientific thinking along these lines until the beginning of the present century.

Laplace postulated that the solar system developed from a large cloud of gas and dust. He assumed that this would contract gravitationally, and that during the contraction process, local turbulent motions within the cloud were smoothed out, leaving a slowly rotating, discus-shaped system. The higher velocities around the equatorial belt would prevent this region from contracting as rapidly as the polar regions and the result would be a central condensation with a thin, equatorial web. Further contraction combined with the conservation of angular momentum would produce an increase in the velocities of the material in the web until the gravitational force toward the center would be unable to cause any more shrinkage.

Laplace held that at this stage in the evolution, a ring of material around the outside of the equatorial web was left behind, rotating at orbital speed, while the rest of the web continued to shrink with an accompanying increase in velocity. When the rotation became rapid enough, a second ring would be sluffed off. This was repeated time after time, until a ring had been left behind for each planet in the solar system. He then assumed that the rings could not be absolutely uniform but that each would have some slight concentration which would gradually draw the other particles into it, sweeping together all the material in a given ring to form a planet. These planets, he hypothesized, all moved around the central sun in essentially the same plane, and in the same direction, their orbits nearly circular. As the larger masses condensed to form the major planets, each of them was to develop a central web, which provided for the fourteen satellites known at that time.

Laplace's Nebular Hypothesis looked so good, at least from a qualitative standpoint, that it was accepted with little question until early in the present century.

DYNAMIC ENCOUNTER THEORIES

Around 1900, T. C. Chamberlin, a geologist, and F. R. Moulton, an astronomer, teamed up to try to provide more definitive mathematical verification for the Laplacian Nebular Hypothesis; however, their calculations seemed to disprove, rather than prove the theory. Their work showed that rather than sluffing off a series of rings, the rotating mass developed spiral arms. Much more damaging than this, however, they found that the massive central sun should retain the major part of the angular momentum of the system. It actually has only 2 per cent of the total. Moulton and Chamberlin felt that Laplace's work could no longer be accepted.

To account for the high angular momentum of the planets, they suggested that a passing star had gone relatively near the sun. This, they contended, would have produced excessively high tides and would have drawn out some of the solar material. As the liberated gases cooled, they were to solidify into vast numbers of small, solid particles, planetesimals, which would be made to revolve around the sun by the attraction of the passing star. Many of them fell back into the sun, giving it the slow rotation which we know today. Those that were left in orbit formed a web which eventually condensed into knots of material at different distances from the sun, the forerunners of today's planets. Satellites resulted from similar equatorial webs of planetesimal material surrounding the more massive planets.

Chamberlin and Moulton assumed that most of the material was initially in rather small pieces and that the planets, as they formed, remained solid. Subsequently, Sir James Jeans and Harold Jeffries favored a few larger masses to provide the nuclei for the planets, which would then grow by sweeping up vast numbers of planetesimals. Jeffries believed that the planets must have become hot enough to go through a liquid stage, thus providing for the sedimentation needed to explain the dense core of the earth and perhaps of other planets. To explain the differences in the chemical composition of the sun and the planets, the lighter gases were assumed to have escaped from the system. In his later work, Jeffries favored a grazing collision between the passing star and the sun, rather than just a near "fly-by." H. N. Russell and R. A. Lyttleton suggested that the sun might have had a companion star at one time and that it was this twin that was hit by the passing star.

Although these dynamic encounter theories were generally accepted for a time, they were not entirely satisfactory. As astronomers learned more about the average distances betwen stars and their motions, it became apparent that the assumed close approach of one star to another would be an exceedingly rare occurrence, so rare, indeed, that among the hundred billion stars in our galaxy there might have been only a few tens of such near misses in the past several billion years. Though this would not rule out the possibility of our sun being one of the few, it does present such overwhelming odds against the theory that it must be viewed with suspicion.

Another question was raised with respect to the condensation of the solar gases into planetesimals. The sun is very hot, under high pressure, and composed largely of hydrogen and helium. Gases liberated from the sun's strong gravitational compression would be certain to expand almost explosively into space, rather than condensing into solid plane-tesimals. Before many decades had passed, astronomers started looking for a theory that involved fewer highly improbable occurrences.

THE PROTOPLANET HYPOTHESIS

During the period from 1900 to 1950, many advances were made in our understanding of turbulent motion in clouds of gas and dust. These enabled C. F. von Weizsacker, in 1944, to propose a theory of solar system evolution which resembled the Laplacian hypothesis in certain respects but had a number of vital differences. Significant modifications to von Weizsacker's theory were suggested by G. P. Kuiper, and the revised theory is known as the protoplanet hypothesis.

The theory begins with a slight condensation in a vast nebulous cloud of gas and dust similar to those found throughout the arms of the Milky Way. No central sun would yet have formed, so there would be no radiation of either light or heat. Since the temperature would not have been much above absolute zero, the velocity of the individual gas and dust particles would have been so low that a comparatively slight gravitational force could initiate a slow contraction. In size, the contracting portion must have been many times the size of the present solar system and would have contained considerably more mass than is presently found in the sun and planets. On photographs of certain regions of the sky, many dark marks are found which look as though they had been drawn with a fine pen and black ink. There is a definite possibility that they might be early stages in the contraction of a nebulous cloud which might later develop into a planetary system similar to our own.

At this stage, the cloud would be far more diffuse than our best laboratory vacuum, but with the gradually increasing density which would result from the slow contraction, the turbulent motions of the various parts of the cloud would eventually become smoothed out and the entire cloud would take on a slow rotation. Because of this rotation, the equatorial regions would contract more slowly than the polar, and what was once an irregular formless cloud would have become a symmetrical rotating mass. It probably had a pronounced central bulge and a rather thick equatorial web containing perhaps 10 per cent of the mass of the entire system.

This heavy web is one significant difference between the protoplanet hypothesis and Laplace's theory. A web containing only about the same amount of mass that is found in the planets today would be too tenuous to develop further condensations, but if the web had between fifty and one hundred times the mass of the present planets and a low temperature, the density would be high enough that we would expect little condensation of gas and dust to form. As they orbit around the central mass, those that are about the same distance from the center would probably collide and merge. After a considerable time we might expect that there would be relatively few large knots of material circling the central mass, all in nearly the same plane and all with relatively circular orbits. Eventually, most of the random material would have been swept up gravitationally, and there would have been one condensation or protoplanet for each planet in the solar system today. It also seems reasonable that each planet should be from one and a half to two times as far from the central mass as the next inner planet.

These protoplanets would have had much the same chemical constitution as the original nebula; that is, they would have been largely hydrogen and helium with the heavier elements making up only a small per cent of the total mass. They would also be much more massive than the planets we know today. Proto-Jupiter, for example may have been from ten to twenty times as massive as Jupiter is now, and proto-earth may have had a thousand times the earth's present mass. The strong tidal effect of the proto-sun probably stopped any rotation the early protoplanets might have had, causing them to keep the same face toward the central mass. Later, as the larger and more distant masses contracted, they probably increased their speed of rotation due to the conservation of angular momentum. We can thus picture the larger protoplanets developing individual equatorial webs, much smaller and less massive than the large web from which the planets formed but of considerably higher density.

The formation of lumps of material within the webs of the proto-planets leads to the formation of protosatellites. Many of them probably had rather eccentric orbits. If the inner satellites at the low points of their orbits brushed through the outer atmosphere of the protoplanet, the satellites' motion would be slowed slightly, and this would tend to make their orbits more nearly circular. Some may have been slowed so much that they spiraled into the protoplanet and became a part of it. The more distant protosatellites remained safely outside the protoplanet atmos-phere and thus retained their somewhat eccentric orbits. Because of their development from the protoplanet's rotating equatorial web, all of the protosatellites revolved in the same direction at this stage.

Within each planet it seems reasonable to assume that sedimenta-tion occured, causing the heavier elements to gravitate to the center of the mass, to be surrounded by a lighter atmosphere composed largely of hydrogen and helium.

Probably at about this stage the contraction of the central protosun caused it to heat up and perhaps even to develop a core dense enough and hot enough to produce nuclear energy. As the proto-sun developed into something similar to the present sun its energy radiated out through the protoplanetary system, producing marked changes. The intensity of the solar radiation varies inversely with the square of the distance, so the nearest protoplanets were brought to a relatively high temperature, resulting in high molecular velocities in their outer regions. Lighter mole-cules have, on the average, much higher velocities than heavier molecules, and thus the hydrogen and helium found it relatively easy to escape from the protoplanet's gravitational hold. Both the electromagnetic and cor-puscular radiation from the sun exerted an outward force on these light-weight particles, sweeping a large fraction of the mass away from the regions of the protoplanets and leaving only the more dense core to develop into the planets we know today.

The more massive protoplanets, located farther from the sun, lost a smaller fraction of their gaseous material. Because of their greater mass they exerted a stronger gravitational force. Because they are farther from the sun, they would not be heated as much as the nearer planets, and thus the gases had a lower molecular velocity. Because of their greater dis-tance, the solar radiation exerted less pressure on the gas molecules to drive them away from the protoplanets. From this we would expect that the outer planets would show a higher concentration of the lighter mole-cules than the planets close to the sun. Though the surface of Venus has not been observed directly it seems very likely that Mercury, Venus, Earth and Mars are all characterized by a relatively solid surface comparable to the lithosphere of the earth. These planets seem to have a much smaller percentage of hydrogen and helium than is found throughout most of the universe, and they have mean densities between 3.8 and 5.5 times the density of water. The outer planets, Jupiter, Saturn, Uranus and Neptune seem to have high percentages of the lighter elements, though at low temperatures they may be frozen into ice. The densities of these large planets range from 0.7 to 1.6 times the density of water. Determinations of the size and mass of Pluto are too uncertain at present to justify its inclusion in this part of the consideration.

The periods of rotation of the various planets also call for explanation, though here the arguments are not entirely conclusive. In the early preplanetary web the particles nearer the center move faster than the particles farther out. As they impinge on a forming protoplanet we might expect that it would be given a clockwise rotation as seen from the north, contrary to the direction in which it is revolving around the central protosun. We have already seen, however, that viscosity within the web and the breaking effect of solar tides would reduce this rotation to the point that the protoplanet probably kept the same side facing the sun. With respect to outer space, the protoplanet would then be making one counterclockwise rotation about its axis in exactly the same time it made one counterclockwise revolution around the proto-sun.

When a figure skater begins a spin with arms extended and then draws his arms in close to his body, his rate of spin increases noticeably. As the mass of his arms is drawn closer to his axis of spin his moment of inertia is reduced, and the rate of spin must increase proportionately in order to maintain a constant angular momentum. Similarly, as a large, diffuse protoplanet contracts, its speed of rotation would have to increase if its angular momentum is to remain unchanged.

Tides in the protoplanet material produced by the gravitational pull of the sun, would act as a brake and slow down the planet's rotation. Tide-raising forces are, approximately, inversely proportional to the cube of the distance between the two bodies. Thus, tides would be strong in the planets nearest the sun, but relatively insignificant in the distant planets. The long periods of Mercury and Venus and the short periods of the outer planets, beginning with Jupiter, would seem to support this explanation. However, if Venus actually does rotate in the direction contrary to that of the rest of the planets, it presents something of a problem.

The removal of the outer atmospheres of the protoplanets would probably affect the satellite systems in two ways. With no gaseous outer layer to slow the satellites' motion when they are nearest the planet, the eccentricities of their orbits would not be subject to further change. The inner satellites which had developed nearly circular orbits would probably remain in orbits of small eccentricity. The more distant moons which had never come in close enough to have their orbits rounded, would probably continue to have eccentric paths. As the mass of the protoplanet is blown away by the solar radiation the gravitational hold on the satellites will weaken, permitting them to spiral out into larger orbits, though they would presumably retain approximately their original shape. It is quite probable that the sharp reduction in the mass from the protoplanet stage would so greatly weaken the planet's gravitational hold that some of the outer satellites might escape from the planet entirely. If this were to happen, they would go into orbit around the sun with a period which might be either longer or shorter than the period of the planet from which they escaped. On each circuit, however, the escaped satellite would pass close to the position it had when it broke away from its primary. If, after perhaps many circuits of the sun, the original planet happened to be in the same general region, the escaped satellite might be recaptured. Depending on the relative positions and speeds of the two bodies, the recaptured satellite might have either direct or retrograde revolution around its primary. The theory thus provides at least a plausible explanation of Jupiter's satellite system, for example, where the inner five satellites have comparatively circular orbits with direct motion, the next three have more eccentric orbits with direct motion, and the outer four have quite eccentric orbits and retrograde motion.

The asteroids remain a puzzle in this and every other theory of planetary formation. Perhaps they were formed from the same type of material as the other planets, but simply never became concentrated in one protoplanet. If those meteorites which give evidence of being fragments of a much larger body are asteroidal in origin, this would imply that there were once larger bodies which were broken up either by explosion or by collision. But, assuming the same mean density as the earth, the total number of suspected asteroids would make a single planet less than 800 miles in diameter, about 1/10 the size of the earth. This seems too small for a bona-fide planet. At least seven satellites in the solar system are larger than this, and four more are almost as large. An explosion in a planet the size of the earth would have had to be so violent that 99.9 per cent of the material blew out of the solar system to leave as little as is presently found in the asteroids. On the other hand, a few score of bodies averaging about 200 miles in diameter would have provided about the right amount of material. At present, however, our knowledge of the asteroids is too fragmentary to result in anything more than pure speculation about their origin.

The origin of comets, too, is highly speculative. To say that they come from a comet reservoir located from 1/5 to 3/5 the distance to the nearest stars simply raises the question of what the reservoir is and how it originated. Perhaps it is simply material that was too peripheral to be drawn into the rotating nebulous mass that developed into the proto-sun and protoplanets. Or perhaps it is composed of the material driven off the protoplanets when the sun started to radiate. This, however, would imply a greater concentration of material in the direction of the plane of the planetary orbits, and the near parabolic comets seem to come relatively uniformly from all parts of the sky.

The accepted belief today is that the nuclei of comets are composed of frozen gases in which large numbers of solid particles are imbedded. Spectra of shower meteors, believed to be associated with comets, indicate the presence of iron, but no positively identified shower meteor has ever been recovered as a meteorite. Perhaps there are vast numbers of solid particles in the region of the reservoir in which the cometary nuclei are forming, or perhaps, in repeated trips through the regions of the asteroids and zodiacal light particles, the comet head has swept up this material. Here again, we can only guess.

SUMMARY

It must be obvious that at the present time there simply is no completely satisfactory explanation of the origin of the solar system. The astronomical origin of the earth must, of course, share this uncertainty. The protoplanet hypothesis explains more things better than any previous theory, but it is far from complete. It is based on a much better understanding of the problem than any of the previous theories, but it will be surprising indeed if it does not undergo significant alterations in the next few decades.

8

The Sun

TOPICS

The sun's interior	The chromosphere
The photosphere	Solar prominences
Sunspots	The sun's corona

The only characteristic that sets the sun apart from the other stars is our nearness to it. Our distance from the sun averages about 92,960,000 miles, and the next nearest star, Proxima Centauri, is some two hundred seventy thousand times that distance. Light reaches us from the sun in about 8 minutes, but requires 4.7 years to make the trip from Proxima Centauri.

The most significant effect of this relative nearness to the sun is, of course, that the earth receives enough heat and light to make it habitable. To the astronomer, though, there are other advantages. Our sun is the only star whose surface can be seen and studied in its various details in our telescopes. All others appear as mere points of light in even our largest instruments, making it impossible to observe separately the characteristics of various parts of the star's surface. On the sun, details as small as a few tens of miles across have been photographed.

When we observe the sun visually, its apparent diameter averages slightly more than 1/2 degree. To have this angular size at a distance of 92,960,000 miles, the linear diameter of the sun must be 864,000 miles, or one hundred nine times the diameter of the earth.

In the zones between 5 and 35 degrees both north and south of the sun's equator a number of sunspots are usually visible. By timing their apparent motion across the sun's disk it is possible to determine the sun's period of rotation. Near the solar equator the period is about 25 days, but it becomes somewhat longer with increasing distance from the equator. Sunspots are not observed at solar latitudes greater than 40 degrees, but spectroscopic observations of the Doppler shift in the light coming from the edges of the disk indicate that the period of rotation near the poles must be close to 35 days. Since the sun is entirely gaseous it does not have to rotate with the same period in all latitudes as it would if it were a solid body, but can "flow" around, with the equatorial regions having a shorter period than the polar zones.

When the position of a sunspot is measured on a number of successive days, it is frequently found that its path is not straight but slightly curved. This results from the fact that the sun's axis of rotation is tilted about 7 degrees away from the perpendicular to the plane of the earth's orbit.

It is convenient to think of the sun as divided into a number of concentric shells: the interior, the photosphere, the chromosphere, the prominences and the corona. It is, however, incorrect to think of each of the divisions as being bounded by a discrete surface. There is, rather, a transitional zone that may be several hundred miles thick within which the characteristics of one layer gradually change to the characteristics of the next.

THE SUN'S INTERIOR

The interior of the sun cannot be studied by direct observation, but theoretical models have been constructed which must be rather close approximations to the actual conditions. These must adequately account for the sun's mass, 333,000 times the mass of the earth; the sun's diameter, 864,000 miles; its surface temperature at the photosphere of about 6,000° Kelvin; its rate of radiation, 3.8×10^{33} ergs per second, or 500,000 million million million horsepower; its probable chemical constitution, 60 to 80 per cent by weight of hydrogen, roughly 20 to 40 per cent helium and 1 to 4 per cent of all the elements other than hydrogen and helium. Of the ninety-two natural elements that have been identified on the earth, the spectroscope has revealed more than sixty on the sun. Most of those that have not been identified are so uncommon here that a similar concentration in the sun would render them undetectable spectroscopically. The uncertainty as to the precise chemical constitution of the interior of the sun is one of the main problems in establishing the conditions on which a solar model is to be calculated.

Most of the solar models agree that the central regions of the sun must have a temperature of approximately 15 million degrees Kelvin (27 million degrees Fahrenheit) with an uncertainty of at most a few million degrees. Pressures near the sun's center may run as high as 7 million million pounds per square inch, equivalent to the weight of a hundred 40,000 ton battle ships concentrated on an area the size of a one-millimeter perforation in a postage stamp. Under these completely incomprehensible conditions protons are being converted into helium nuclei, producing energy at the rate of 5 x 10^{23} horsepower. The manner in which this is accomplished will be considered in greater detail in the next chapter in connection with the production of stellar energy.

Quite obviously, the energy that is produced in the central region of the sun must be transported through successively larger and cooler shells, until it is finally radiated from the sun's photosphere. From the center outward for about 2/3 the distance to the photosphere the energy radiated by each shell is absorbed by the next larger and slightly cooler shell, which in turn radiates the energy to the shell surrounding it. For the outer third of the sun's radius, the radiative transfer seems to be replaced by convective transfer. Here the gases become heated at the lower levels, and then rise, carrying the energy with them. Gases that have cooled at the upper levels sink to greater depths, where they again absorb energy and rise. Some investigators feel there is a second layer of radiative transfer just beneath the photosphere, though observations of the apparent surface of the sun certainly indicate that even here there is an appreciable amount of vertical convection.

It seems almost certain that the next few decades will improve our understanding of the details of the sun's interior. The clarification of these details will not, however, alter the fact that tremendous amounts of energy are being released continuously and steadily in the sun's interior and that in some way this energy is transported outward to be radiated into space from the apparent surface of the sun, the photosphere.

THE PHOTOSPHERE

When we watch a sunset on a clear evening, the light of the sun is frequently so dimmed by its long passage through our atmosphere that the disk is not uncomfortably bright. It will usually appear quite red, because the shorter, blue rays have been scattered by our air. The disk looks round and hard-edged, as though there were a definite surface there. This apparent surface of the sun is called the photosphere.

The photosphere of the sun, however, is not a discrete surface. Normally, an hydrogen atom consists of one proton and one electron. If all the hydrogen in the outer layers of the sun were of this type,

Figure 8.1. The photosphere of the sun, photographed in white light, left, and in red Hα hydrogen light. Photograph from the Mount Wilson and Palomar Observatories.

we would be able to see much farther down into the sun's interior, but under the conditions in the photosphere, a minute fraction of the hydrogen atoms will have acquired an extra electron, becoming negative hydrogen ions. These are quite opaque to radiation coming from the interior of the sun and limit the depth to which we can see into the sun's gases. The photosphere is thus a layer slightly less than 200 miles thick within which all the sunlight we see originates.

Were it not for the overlying gases, the light emitted by the photosphere would have a continuous spectrum. In a spectroscope it would appear to be an unbroken band of color extending from the reddest red to the bluest blue that can be observed. But the gases in the outer part of the photosphere and in the regions immediately above absorb just those frequencies or colors which they are capable of emitting, so that the sunlight which reaches the earth has a dark line, or absorption spectrum. By measuring the exact wavelengths of these absorption lines and matching them to the observed or calculated wavelengths of the spectral lines of the various elements, the astronomer is able to determine the chemical constitution of the sun.

The sun must *never* be observed through a telescope or binoculars without suitable filters to reduce the intensity of the radiation. Failure to heed this warning is very likely to result in a permanent blind spot on the retina or to cause even more serious damage.

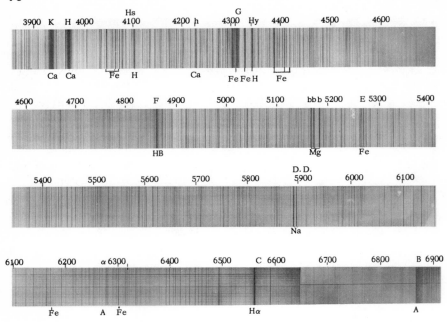

Figure 8.2. The spectrum of the sun. Photograph from the Mount Wilson and Palomar Observatories.

When the sun is observed either visually or photographically with suitable equipment, the photosphere is found to have a mottled appearance, like a single layer of rice grains spread on a piece of gray cardboard. Granulations as small as 300 miles in diameter have been photographed from an elevation of 80,000 feet above the earth's surface by a balloon-borne telescope. From this height, the disturbing effects of our atmosphere are almost entirely eliminated.

The individual granules appear bright because they are the tops of vertically rising columns of hotter gases coming up through the other gases at speeds of approximately 2 miles a second. After the gases cool a bit they appear less bright and probably settle back down, to be reheated and rise again. Any individual granule will normally last between 5 and 10 minutes.

SUNSPOTS

There are scattered records extending back thousands of years of small dark spots seen against the face of the sun at times when atmospheric haze permitted the sun to be viewed directly. Early in the seventeenth century, Galileo reported observing sunspots with his telescopes. In the three and a half centuries since Galileo's time they have been studied closely, but there are still many unanswered questions relating to their exact nature and cause.

A typical sunspot consists of a central relatively dark umbra, frequently quite irregular in shape, which may be anywhere from a few hundred to several tens of thousands of miles across. This is surrounded by a somewhat lighter region, the penumbra. The umbra is about 1500° K cooler than the photosphere, so it looks quite dark by comparison, but its temperature of 4500° K makes it very bright by terrestrial standards. It is worth noting that the transitions from the umbra to the penumbra, and from the penumbra to the photosphere are quite sudden and well-defined, rather than gradual, as might be anticipated.

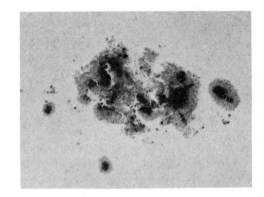

Figure 8.3. A large sunspot group, May 17, 1951. Photograph from the Mount Wilson and Palomar Observatories.

An individual spot may last anywhere from a few days to several weeks. A few have been known to last for several months. Due to the rotation of the sun, a series of observations on any individual spot cannot last longer than two weeks, though after a spot disappears at the western limb of the sun it may be carried around the back to reappear at the eastern limb about two weeks later.

Sunspots commonly appear in groups which may consist of scores of individual spots. The first indication of the development of a sunspot group is the appearance of two small clusters of spots located east and west of each other. Within a few days one of the spots in each group will have become appreciably larger than its companions, and the two groups will have drifted apart until their separation is roughly 75 to 100 thousand miles. In about a week the groups will normally start a slow decline. The smaller spots shrink and disappear first, leaving only the two larger spots. Tongues of gas are frequently seen to cut across the more easterly or following spot, which then gradually fades from sight. The leading or westerly (as we see it) spot then slowly shrinks until it can no longer be seen.

Doppler shifts indicate that there is an out-flowing of the material in the photosphere immediately surrounding the spot. Sequence photography has shown clouds of gas at higher levels which were drawn into the centers of the spots as though they were being sucked into a vortex. Polarization of spectrum lines reveals that the sunspots have magnetic fields several thousand times as strong as the earth's and that the leading and following spot of any group are normally of opposite magnetic polarity. It is believed that the strong magnetic field blocks the flow of energy from the sun's interior, producing a local "cool" area.

A century and a half ago, astronomers began counting the number of sunspots visible each day, and it was found that their numbers reach a maximum about every 11.2 years, though the interval from one maximum to the next has varied from nine to fourteen years. Not only do the numbers of spots vary, but their positions change in phase with the count. At the beginning of a cycle, a few spots appear in two zones about 35 degrees north and south of the solar equator. Each spot lives out its life at approximately the latitude at which it started, but successive spots not only increase in number but are located progressively nearer the solar equator. In about four years, the number of spots will reach its maximum and start to fall off, though the zones in which they are found will continue to approach the sun's equator. As the cycle finally dies out, the last spots are occurring in solar latitudes 5 degrees north and south. Spots are not found directly on the sun's equator. The zones in the two hemispheres are symmetrically placed with respect to the solar equator, and as the last spots of one cycle are occurring in the near-equatorial regions, the first spots of the next cycle are likely to become visible in about the same regions in which the previous cycle started.

With special magnetometers we can measure the strength of the magnetic fields of sunspots, and when these are included the picture becomes even more intriguing. In any particular cycle, the leading spots in one hemisphere will normally all have the same magnetic polarity, and the leading spots in the other hemisphere will have the opposite polarity. Following spots in both hemispheres will have opposite polarity from their leading spots. In the next eleven-year cycle, all the polarities will be reversed. For the cycle which ended in 1965, the leading spots in the northern hemisphere were north-seeking poles; those in the southern hemisphere were south-seeking. In the following cycle, the leading poles in the northern hemisphere were south-seeking; those in the southern hemisphere, north-seeking.

For scores of years, astronomers have groped for some theory that would explain these remarkable characteristics. Not until the early 1960s did H. W. Babcock of the Mount Wilson and Palomar Observatories suggest what seems to be a reasonable explanation. In 1964-1965 there were very few sunspots, and during this "quiet sun" period tests were made at the Kitt Peak National Observatory in Arizona which appear to support the new theory in considerable detail. New, highly sensitive instruments should add a wealth of observational data within the next decade.

Babcock's explanation is based on the sun's magnetic field and the way it is influenced by the solar rotation. At the beginning of a cycle we may think of the lines of force of the magnetic field running north and south, imbedded in the solar gases relatively near the photosphere, say in the outer tenth of the sun's radius. Because the ionized gases of the sun are good conductors of electricity, the lines of force would be "frozen in," that is, they would be carried along by any drift of the solar material like a piece of string in thick syrup. The equatorial regions of the sun are rotating more rapidly than the higher latitudes, so the

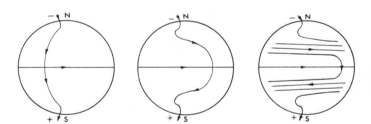

Figure 8.4. Diagram illustrating Horace W. Babcock's explanation of the cause of sunspot zones, magnetic polarity of sunspot groups and so forth.

portions of the lines of force near the equator are carried around more rapidly than the portions farther from the equator. This wrapping around produces a concentration of the lines of force, something of a magnetic rope, which first becomes relatively strong at latitudes about 35 degrees north and south of the solar equator. Kinks in the rope, perhaps produced by turbulence in the solar gases, cause local concentrations in the magnetic field, and where these become most intense, magnetic buoyancy causes them to float to the surface. Whenever the strand breaks through the photosphere we get a dipole effect, producing the two sunspot groups of opposite polarity. Since all the groups in one hemisphere are produced by similar breaks in what is fundamentally the same magnetic rope, the magnetic polarities in the various groups will be similarly oriented. Because the magnetic field points in opposite directions in the two hemispheres, the orientation of the magnetic polarities in the groups north and south of the equator will be reversed.

As the sunspot groups break through the photosphere, they tend to neutralize the magnetic fields in their latitude, but the continuing rotation keeps building field concentrations that gradually approach the equator, causing the sunspot zones to migrate. The solar rotation is so uniform near the equator that no significant magnetic build-up is produced and thus no spots are formed.

As sunspots and solar turbulence break up the uniformity of the field, there is a tendency for the magnetic field of the following spot to drift poleward slightly more than that of the leading spot. By the time the quiet sun stage has been reached, this selective drift will have caused the general magnetic field of the sun to have reversed its polarity from what it was at the preceding quiet sun period. Thus the magnetic polarity of the leading spots in both hemispheres will reverse with each successive active sun period.

It has been observed that during the periods of maximum numbers of sunspots, frequently called the "active sun," the earth receives slightly more solar radiation than during the times when the sunspots are few in number. Sharp variations in the strength of the earth's magnetic field, more frequent and more brilliant auroral displays, greater amounts of radio static and interference with long distance radio communication due to the disruption of ionized layers in the earth's atmosphere also seem to occur with an active sun. The occurrence of sunspots must therefore be considered to be but one of several effects produced by an active sun.

Occasionally, a small area of the sun will brighten to many times the luminosity of the surrounding area, producing a solar flare. Its rise to maximum brightness occupies only a few minutes and will usually start to fade almost at once, disappearing completely within a few hours at the most. These solar flares release tremendous amounts of energy within a short time. It has been suggested that they may be produced when energy that has been bottled up in the sun by a powerful magnetic field breaks through to the surface, but the actual mechanism which produces them is certainly not yet completely understood.

THE CHROMOSPHERE

Shortly after the invention of the telescope, several observers commented about a brilliant red rim that was seen around the edge of the sun for a second or so just when the moon completely covered the photosphere at the very beginning and end of a solar eclipse. The spectrum of this chromosphere was first observed about a century ago and was found to be a bright-line emission spectrum, with the bright lines corresponding in general to the dark lines normally found in the solar spectrum. The color of the chromosphere is due to the strong red emission line of hydrogen, having a wavelength of 6563 A or 0.00006563 cm. Up to the beginning of the present century the chromosphere could be investigated only during the few brief seconds at each solar eclipse, but now the spectroheliographs and coronagraphs make it possible to observe it at any time.

Though the chromosphere is usually thought of as being a layer perhaps 5000 miles thick, it has no definite boundaries. On the inside it is an extension of the photosphere, beginning in an indefinite region in which the negative hydrogen ions are so infrequent that there is relatively little absorption of energy. On the outside, it blends almost imperceptibly with the sun's inner corona. When the outer part of the chromosphere is viewed at the edge of the sun's disk, its surface is frequently seen to contain many spicules, small jetlike columns of rising gas, making the chromosphere appear as though it were covered with blades of red grass.

In regions of relatively strong magnetic fields, commonly found near sunspot activity but occasionally in areas where no sunspots are visible, we frequently see what appear to be clouds giving off strong radiation as the result of emission from hydrogen or calcium atoms. They probably are not isolated clouds of these elements but rather regions in the general solar atmosphere in which the hydrogen or calcium atoms have been excited to the level at which they emit light. Occasionally, they appear darker than the rest of the surface, indicating strong absorption in these wavelengths. They were formerly called flocculi but are now more commonly termed plages. Occasionally, plages will emit light of many frequencies, so that they can be seen in white light without the use of special equipment. They are then called faculae.

It would be expected that the chromosphere would be appreciably cooler than the photosphere, but spectroscopic studies show that the temperature increases in the chromosphere to a value of close to 100,000° K in its upper layers. This is, however, a kinetic temperature, based on the amount of molecular activity. The density of the lower part of the chromosphere is only a fraction of a millionth of that of our air at sea

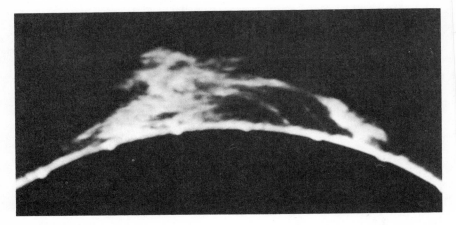

Figure 8.5. A large solar prominence 132,000 miles high photographed in calcium light August 18, 1947. Photograph from the Mount Wilson and Palomar Observatories.

level, and it decreases rapidly with elevation. Thus, though the kinetic temperature may be high, the actual heat content may be quite low.

SOLAR PROMINENCES

Prior to the development of spectroheliographs and coronagraphs in the present century, solar prominences, like the chromosphere, could be observed only during a total solar eclipse. Though they could some-times be seen with the naked eye, the best observations were telescopic. The prominences looked like red protuberances extending outward thousands of miles from the chromosphere. The color, like that of the chromosphere, is due to a strong red emission line of hydrogen.

Some prominences are quite active, showing noticeable changes in a relatively few minutes. Others remain quiescent for considerable periods of time. Certain types seem to form like a cloud in the lower corona and rain material down onto the chromosphere. The

Figure 8.6 The solar corona photographed at the total eclipse of June 8, 1918, Green River, Wyoming. Photograph from the Mount Wilson and Palomar Observatories.

relatively uncommon eruptive prominences appear to rise from the chromosphere into the inner corona with velocities of up to 450 miles a second, and occasional individuals have been observed to attain elevations in excess of 1 million miles. When they are observed silhoutted against the sun's disk with a spectroheliograph they frequently appear to be dark, irregular filaments. Certain types of prominences are found most frequently in regions of considerable sunspot activity.

THE SUN'S CORONA

The corona is the outermost region of the sun, and it has been observed for thousands of years during total solar eclipses when the moon blotted out the much more brilliant photosphere. Since 1930, astronomers have been able to observe the inner and brighter part of the corona with coronagraphs, special instruments that, in effect, produce an artificial eclipse.

Some of the bright lines in the spectrum of the corona remained a mystery until 1942, when they were identfied as lines of calcium, iron and nickel atoms that had lost from nine to thirteen electrons. Such a high degree of ionization indicates that the gas must be extremely rarified and that it must have a temperature of approximately 1,000,000° K. It must be remembered, however, that this is a kinetic temperature and that because of the extremely low density of the material the actual heat content of the corona is small.

The size of the corona is difficult to determine and depends in some measure on how it is defined. Photographs taken during total solar eclipses clearly show the corona extending well over 1 million miles above the photosphere. Astronomers using radio telescopes on distant objects have found that the incoming signals were noticeably weakened when the sun came within about 5 degrees, or roughly 10 million miles of their line of observation. The loss of signal strength could be caused by a rarified solar atmosphere of ionized particles and could be interpreted as indicating that the outer corona has an approximate diameter of 20 million miles. We also know that in addition to the heat and light which we receive from the sun, the earth is being continuously bombarded by corpuscular radiation, mostly protons and electrons, which noticeably increase in intensity following strong solar activity such as solar flares. The effect on our atmosphere, noted in the form of auroras, radio interference, and so forth, normally follows the visual appearance of the solar activity by about one day. The particles must therefore be traveling 93 million miles in twenty-four hours, or about 1 thousand miles a second. If the particles comprising this solar wind are to be considered part of the corona, then it must extend well past the earth and have a diameter in excess of 200 million miles.

Photographs taken during total solar eclipses reveal that the shape of the corona differs noticeably when the sun is active and when it is passive. Around the time of sunspot minima the corona shows rather clearly defined streamers. With the active sun, coincident with the times of sunspot maxima, the corona seems to fill in and become almost circular.

In summary, this chapter should make one thing evident: that although we know more about the sun than about any other star, much more work is needed before we can feel we understand it completely.

CHAPTER

9

Stellar Observations

TOPICS

Trigonometric parallaxes

Proper motion, radial velocity and space
    velocity

Solar motion

Apparent magnitudes

Absolute magnitudes

Stellar spectra

The Russell-Hertzsprung diagram

Diameters of stars

Stellar masses

On any clear, moonless night an observer should be able to see between 2500 and 3000 individual stars with the naked eye. Some will look much brighter than others, and a few of the brightest may appear blue, yellow or red. Night after night and century after century they seem to maintain the same positions relative to one another. Beyond this, the naked-eye observer can learn little about them.

If we are to know what stars really are, we must know their distance from us, their true motions, their sizes, masses and temperatures and the amount of energy they radiate. This chapter is intended to show how astronomers are able to learn these facts. In Chapter 10 we will see how this information is combined with the knowledge gained by the atomic physicist to enable us to describe the birth, life and death of a star.

TRIGONOMETRIC PARALLAXES

If we photograph the same region of the sky with a long focus telescope on two dates separated by an interval of six months, the two observing positions will be separated by about 186 million miles. The apparent position of a star in the sky should differ slightly on the two photographs, and the amount of the change will depend on the star's distance. The displacement will be relatively large for a near star and smaller for a distant one. An extremely distant star, and therefore usually very faint, should theoretically show a very tiny change of position, but our instruments are not accurate enough to measure it.

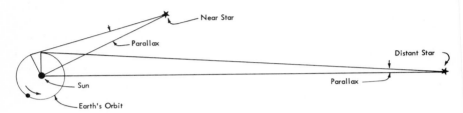

Figure 9.1. The parallax of a star is the angular semidiameter of the earth's orbit as seen from the star.

The parallax of a star is defined as the angular semidiameter of the earth's orbit as seen from the star and is equal to half the total displacement of the star as observed from opposite sides of the earth's orbit. The largest parallax ever measured is only 0.76 second of arc for the star Proxima Centauri. This is equal to the angle that would be subtended by a foot ruler at a distance of 51.4 miles from the observer. For stars so distant that their measured parallaxes are less than 0.01 second, the unavoidable errors in the measurement are as large or larger than the parallax and the determination has little meaning.

A convenient unit of stellar distance is the parsec, which is the distance at which a star would have a parallax of exactly one second. It is equal to 206,265 A.U., or about 20 million million miles. The distance to any star in parsecs is equal to one divided by its parallax in seconds. Another frequently used distance unit for stars is the light year, which is the distance a beam of light would travel in one year, or about 6 million million miles. One parsec equals 3.26 light years.

It is unfortunate that trigonometric parallaxes are useless for stars more than 100 parsecs from the earth, but there are several thousand within that distance whose parallaxes have been measured, and these provide the information needed to set up other distance-measuring systems.

PROPER MOTION, RADIAL VELOCITY AND SPACE VELOCITY

The constellations appear today almost exactly as they did two thousand years ago. We are thus justified in speaking of the "fixed stars."

Actually, each star does have its own random motion or space velocity and may be moving several tens of miles per second with respect to its neighbors. If they were not so extremely distant from the earth, the sky would present a constantly changing spectacle.

By comparing two photographs of a given region taken several years apart we can measure the angular rate at which a star is moving across the sky, its proper motion. Probably less than 1/10 the nearer stars have changed their positions by 1/10 the diameter of the moon in the last two thousand years. If we have a star's proper motion and know its parallax we can find its tangential velocity, the linear speed in miles per second with which it is moving at right angles to the line of sight. By the use of a spectrograph and the Doppler shift we can measure the speed with which a star is moving toward or away from the earth, its radial velocity. The tangential velocity and radial velocity may then be combined to yield the star's space velocity, that is, the direction and speed with which it is moving with respect to the earth.

Figure 9.2. The space velocity of a star produces its radial velocity, tangential velocity and proper motion.

SOLAR MOTION

If other stars have space velocities, it would seem quite reasonable to suspect that our sun might have its own individual motion with respect to neighboring stars, and it does. The average radial velocity of a large number of stars in the region of the constellation Hercules, measured by the Doppler shifts in their spectra, is −12 miles per second, indicating that our distance from them is decreasing at this rate. The average radial velocity of stars in the opposite section of the sky, south of the constellation of Orion, is +12 miles per second, showing that the distance between the sun and the average of the stars in that part of the sky is increasing. The obvious explanation is that the sun's space velocity, usually called the solar motion, is in the direction toward the constellation of Hercules and that the velocity is about 12 miles per second.

APPARENT MAGNITUDES

In the second century B.C. Hipparchus prepared a catalog of just over a thousand stars in which he called the twenty brightest first magnitude. the next fainter but larger group second magnitude and so on, with the faintest stars that could be seen with the naked eye designated as sixth magnitude.

When it became possible to make accurate measurements of the brightness of the stars it was noted that the average first magnitude star in Hipparchus' catalog was about one hundred times as bright as his average sixth magnitude star. The factor of one hundred times in brightness for a difference of five magnitudes was therefore adopted as the standard. To keep a uniform ratio between individual magnitudes the ratio for the difference of one magnitude was set at the fifth root of 100, 2.512, or about 2 1/2. Thus the brightness difference for one magnitude is 2 1/2, for two magnitudes 6 1/4, for three magnitudes 16, for four magnitudes 40, and for five magnitudes exactly 100. When telescopes enabled us to see fainter stars the scale was extended, and stars of apparent magnitude +24 can be photographed with our largest instruments. For objects brighter than the average first magnitude star the scale was extended in the negative direction. Venus reaches a magnitude of −4.4, and the apparent magnitude of the sun is −26.7.

ABSOLUTE MAGNITUDES

When we wish to consider the physical characteristics of a star we are much more interested in how bright it actually is than we are in how bright it happens to look to us. Its apparent magnitude must depend not only on its actual candle power but also on its distance.

The absolute magnitude of a star is defined as the apparent magnitude which the star would have if its distance were exactly 10 parsecs. Stars nearer than 10 parsecs would have to be moved farther away, so their absolute magnitude would be fainter (a larger number) than their apparent magnitude. Stars farther away than 10 parsecs would be brought nearer so their absolute magnitude would be brighter (a smaller number) than their apparent magnitude.

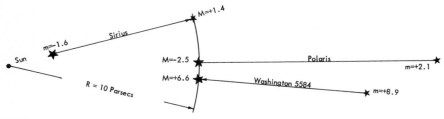

Figure 9.3. The absolute magnitude of any star is the apparent magnitude that star would have if its distance were 10 parsecs.

The absolute magnitude of the sun is +4.86, and it is interesting to note that if the sun's distance actually were 10 parsecs it would be one of the fainter stars visible to the naked eye. Except for novae during an outburst, the brightest stars known have absolute magnitudes of about −5 and are thus 10,000 times as luminous as our sun. The faintest stars known have absolute magnitudes of about +15, making them only 1/10,000 as bright as the sun.

STELLAR SPECTRA

The spectra of literally thousands of stars have been photographed and almost without exception they are dark line absorption spectra similar to the sun's, indicating that the light we observed originated at the star's photosphere, and then passed through a stellar atmosphere where the dark lines were produced by the absorption of specific colors or wavelengths of light.

Since each element in the gaseous form emits and absorbs a specific set of wavelengths, identification of the lines in a stellar spectrum indicates what elements are present. The relative intensities of the various lines of a particular element provide a key to the star's temperature. A comparison of the intensities of the lines of different elements indicates the amounts of the various elements present in the star's atmosphere. An atom with its full complement of orbital electrons is said to be neutral. If an atom absorbs a sufficient amount of energy, one or more of the orbital electrons can be stripped from the atom, and it is then said to be ionized. The ionized atom has a different set of spectral lines from the neutral atom of the same element. By noting if the lines are all shifted from their normal positions toward the blue or the red end of the spectrum, the Doppler shift lets us determine how rapidly the star is approaching or receding from the earth. Thus a study of a star's spectrum tells us its physical condition, its chemical constitution, its temperature, its degree of ionization and its radial velocity.

Stellar spectra reveal a surprising but very significant fact. The chemical constitution of the vast majority of the stars is almost identical. They are mostly hydrogen with a little helium and only extremely small amounts of all the other elements. The differences in the spectra of various stars result almost entirely from their differences in temperature. Variations in pressure and in the very small amounts of the heavier elements present are significant in the study of stellar evolution, but the prime cause of the differences in stellar spectra is temperature.

Early in the study of stellar spectra it seemed desirable to arrange them into a logical sequence with minimal differences between adjacent spectra and to assign letter designations to various sections of the series. Because some plates which were later found to be faulty were included in the original sequence and because relatively little was known about the nature of stellar spectra at that time, the designations did not end up in a strict alphabetical order, but the letters originally assigned have been retained. The sequence of stellar spectra is now recognized to be in the order O, B, A, F, G, K, M, with a few stars in subgroups R, N and S. (The order of the letters can be remembered by the sentence, Oh Be A Fine Girl, Kiss Me.) The B-type stars, for example, are hot blue stars with temperatures between 11,000° and 25,000° K and show strong helium and hydrogen lines. The G-type, which includes the sun, are yellow stars with temperatures from 5000° to 6000° K and have strong metallic lines, particularly those of calcium, in their spectra. The M-type stars are quite red as a result of their low temperatures of from 2000° to 3400° K, cool enough that some chemical compounds can exist, so that their spectra show molecular bands as well as the lines of various elements.

THE RUSSELL-HERTZSPRUNG DIAGRAM

A most interesting and revealing representation of some of the stellar characteristics can be made by plotting the absolute magnitudes of a large number of stars against their spectral class, Figure 9.5. When this is done for stars in the vicinity of our sun, a large percentage fall into a diagonal band running from upper left to lower right, which has been called the main sequence. The stars in the upper left are very bright, large, hot and blue, and are called blue giants. Our sun is found roughly in the middle of the main sequence. In the lower right, the stars are faint, small, cool and red, and are frequently referred to as the red dwarfs. The stars in the upper right section are very large, bright, cool and red, and are the red giants. The stars at the top right are extremely large and bright, though still red, and are the red supergiants. In the lower left-hand region there are a few stars which, though yellow or blue and quite hot, are so small that they are very faint; these are the white dwarfs. The full significance of the Russell-Hertzsprung diagram will become more apparent in the next chapter when we consider the physical nature and evolution of stars.

THE DIAMETERS OF STARS

The stars are all so distant that they appear as mere points of light in even our largest telescopes. Thus, we cannot make direct measure-

Figure 9.4. The basic spectral classification of stars. Photograph from the Mount Wilson and Palomar Observatories.

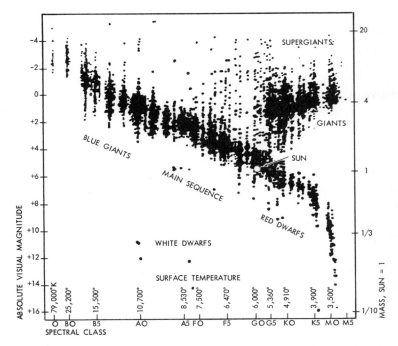

Figure 9.5. The Russell-Hertzsprung spectrum-luminosity diagram for Type I population stars.

ments of their diameters. However, from material which has already been considered, their sizes can be found.

The absolute magnitude of a star is really a measure of its total rate of radiation. Our sun, for example, with an absolute magnitude of +4.86, is radiating almost 4 x 10^{33} ergs per second. A star of absolute magnitude −5 would be radiating ten thousand times this rapidly, and a star of absolute magnitude +15 would be radiating at only 1/10,000 this rate.

From Stefan's law we know that the number of ergs per second given off by each square centimeter of a perfect radiator is found by $E = 0.00005672\ T^4$. The absolute temperature, T, of a star can be found from its spectrum. We can thus find the amount of energy being radiated by each square centimeter of the star's surface.

If we divide the total radiation of a star, obtained from its absolute magnitude, by the rate of radiation per square centimeter, obtained from the temperature, the quotient will be the area of the star's radiating surface in square centimeters. Since the surface of a sphere is 3.1416 times the square of its diameter, the size of a star is readily determined.

The range in the sizes of the stars is quite surprising. Some of the white dwarfs are believed to be of about the same size as the larger planets in the solar system. At the other extreme, the largest of the red supergiants are hundreds of millions of miles in diameter. Antares, for example, is about four hundred eighty times as big as our sun. If our sun were at the center of Antares, then Mercury, Venus, Earth and Mars could all move in their orbits inside the star, and Mars would still be 50 million miles beneath the surface.

STELLAR MASSES

Thousands of binary star systems are known in which two stars are revolving about their common center of gravity, held in their orbits by their gravitational attraction for each other. If the stars are massive they will move more rapidly and have a shorter period for a given separation than if they are relatively low in mass. On the basis of Newton's law of gravitation, it can be shown that the sum of the masses of the two stars, given in units of the sun's mass, multiplied by the square of their period of revolution in years is equal to the cube of their separation in astronomical units, that is, $(M_1 + M_2)P^2 = D^3$. Both the periods and separations have been determined for a large number of binary systems, and from these the masses of the two stars have been determined. Although there are a few exceptions among the giants, the vast bulk of the stars have masses ranging from a tenth to ten solar masses.

10

The Life of a Star

TOPICS

STAR-BUILDING MATERIAL

No one has ever been able to give a scientific explanation of how matter and energy were originally created. Therefore, as we attempt to explain the formation of stars we will simply have to assume that the material from which they were developed was already in existence. The most elemental situation which can be imagined would seem to be a vast cloud of dust and gas of extremely low density. Many parts of our Milky Way Galaxy contain just such clouds, the galactic nebulae. The fact that young stars are frequently found intimately involved in these clouds furnishes at least a degree of support for the assumption that they provide the material from which stars are produced.

We will start, then, with vast clouds of gas and dust stretching on for parsec after parsec, some regions more concentrated than others but with the most dense portions millions of times more rarified than our best laboratory vacuum. This, we believe, is the nursery in which stars are born.

EXPANSION VERSUS CONTRACTION

Within a galactic nebula each gas molecule and speck of dust will have an individual motion which is the result of its thermal energy. If the temperature is high the particles will be moving rapidly, but if it is low the particles will have relatively slow velocities. At a temperature of 1° K, for example, the average hydrogen molecule would be moving with a speed of only about 100 yards a second. These thermal velocities would tend to make a cloud disperse and become even more rarified.

Newton showed there is a force of attraction between every pair of particles in the universe which is proportional to the product of their masses and inversely proportional to the square of the distance between them. The attraction between two individual gas molecules a million miles apart would certainly be insignificant, but if we picture a hydrogen molecule, for example, located near the edge of a vast cloud of material, the infinitesimal attractions of each of the countless billions of particles within the cloud would all be acting in the same general direction and their combined pull might be large enough to overcome the random thermal velocities of the outlying molecules and cause them to move toward the center of the cloud. If a cloud is extremely rarified it would have to be tremendously large for its gravitational pull to initiate contraction. A cloud of somewhat higher density could be much smaller and actually less massive and still be able to exert the gravitational force needed to start a contraction.

Figure 10.1. Dark globules which can be seen in this photograph of the Lagoon Nebula may be prestellar concentrations. Lick Observatory photograph.

We may thus picture a cloud so rarified that it is almost a perfect vacuum but so large that it may be hundreds of light years across. If its temperature is low it may well experience a slow contraction, thus reducing the size of the cloud and at the same time increasing its density. Once the density has passed some critical value, smaller knots of material may become gravitationally stable and start to contract, forming local regions of higher-than-average density, like lumps in mashed potatoes. This process of increasing density and the production of smaller units of condensation may be repeated many times until finally the individual globules have masses comparable to the mass of an individual star, usually between a tenth and ten times the mass of the sun. Photographs in certain regions of the sky show tiny dark markings which many astronomers suspect may be just such globules on their way to becoming stars.

THE HELMHOLTZ CONTRACTION

During these initial stages and for some time thereafter, the temperatures must be close to absolute zero. Since there would be no source of light, the contraction would go on in complete darkness. As the distance between the outer molecules and the center of the cloud diminishes there would be an increase in the gravitational pull toward the center. Whenever a gas is compressed there is a corresponding increase in temperature. As the energy produced by the contraction of the cloud is converted to heat energy, the central regions of the cloud, where the weight of the overlying gases produce the highest pressures, will begin to warm up. At this point the star will begin to radiate in the far infrared, or heat regions, though it is still far too cool to give off light that could be seen.

As the contraction continues, the density, pressure and temperature increase, and eventually the star may be radiating light visible to the human eye. The increasing pressure offers a force which opposes the gravitational contracting force and the shrinking of the star proceeds at a slower rate. The heat from the center of the star works out to the surface and is radiated away, tending to cool the star and thus reducing the pressure, but the gravitational pull maintains the slow contraction and keeps the center of the star hot and radiating.

This production of energy by the shrinking of a star is known as the Helmholtz contraction. For stars as massive as the sun it can produce central temperatures as high as 1,000,000° K. The amount of energy needed to keep the sun shining at its present rate would be produced if its radius were decreasing by only 140 feet a year. A century ago, it was believed that this Helmholtz contraction was the only source of energy for our sun and all the other stars, and it was calculated that the contraction of our sun from a very large cloud to its present size would have provided a constant flow of energy for 50 million years. When it was proposed this seemed to provide an adequate time scale, but we now know that life has been on the earth for between 600 and 800 million years. Obviously, there must be some source of solar and stellar energy besides the Helmholtz contraction.

MATTER AND ENERGY

In 1905 Albert Einstein announced his famous $E = mc^2$, indicating that matter and energy are two forms of the same thing and that tremendous amounts of energy are released if matter is annihilated as matter and transformed into energy. For example, one ounce of anything (air, water, sand,) converted entirely into energy would provide enough power to lift the 81,120-ton Washington Monument, together with its 36,912-ton base to a height of over 1500 miles. Here is a source which is adequate to explain the tremendous amounts of energy being radiated by the stars.

Though the nucleus of an atom is made up of protons and neutrons, the mass of the nucleus is less than the sum of the masses of the individual protons and neutrons of which it is made. An helium nucleus has a mass of 4.00278 mass units, but the two protons and two neutrons of which it is composed have a total mass of 4.04522 units. When the protons and neutrons combine to form the helium nucleus about 1 per cent of the mass is transformed into energy. Only 1 pound of protons and neutrons combining into helium nuclei would produce enough energy to provide 1000 kilowatts of power continuously for more than one hundred thirty-five years.

The difference between the mass of the nucleus and the mass of the component parts increases as we go to the heavier elements as far as iron, the twenty-sixth element. Within this range the combination of two lighter elements to form a heavier one always results in the transformation of some of the mass into energy. This is well illustrated by the fusion in an hydrogen bomb. Beyond iron the process reverses, and when two nuclei combine additional energy must be added to form the heavier atom, or if a heavier atom splits into two lighter ones the excess mass is given off as energy. The release of energy that is coupled with the fission of uranium 235 in our first atomic bombs illustrates the heavy atom reactions.

STELLAR ENERGY

Nuclear reactions are not believed to be significant in the interiors of the stars until the Helmholtz contraction has raised the central temperature to the order of 1,000,000° K. At this temperature, the atoms would be completely stripped of their orbital electrons, and the reactions would take place exclusively between atomic nuclei. In the range from 1,000,000 to 7,000,000° K, half a dozen or more reactions can occur between hydrogen nuclei and the nuclei of helium, lithium, beryllium and boron, building heavier atoms and always transforming the slight excess mass into energy. As the conditions favorable for each of the reactions are reached, the energy released helps build up the central temperature and pressure of the star, slowing or stopping the star's contraction until the atoms used in that reaction are all consumed. Further contraction then increases the central temperature and pressure until the next reaction can begin. During these stages in the star's evolution there is a plentiful supply of hydrogen, but the amounts of the other elements are quite limited, thus putting a ceiling on the total amount of energy that each of the individual reactions can produce.

When all of the lighter elements except hydrogen and helium have been used up, there seem to be no energy sources available until the contraction of the star has raised its central temperature to 15,000,000° or higher. Then several reactions can occur. A normal hydrogen nucleus is simply a proton, and two of these can combine by the so-called proton-proton reaction as the first of several steps which eventually result in the building of helium atoms. By a completely different process four protons combine with nuclei of carbon, nitrogen and oxygen in a series of six nuclear reactions. In the final stage, an helium nucleus splits off and leaves a carbon nucleus to start another cycle. In any of these processes the net result is that four hydrogen nuclei, or protons with a total mass of 4.03036 units combine to form an helium nucleus with a mass of 4.00278 units, and the difference of 0.02758 units, or about 7/10 of one per cent of the original mass, is transformed into energy. These are the reactions which are producing the sun's energy at the present time. Since hydrogen is the only element consumed, and since in stars like our sun hydrogen may constitute up to 80 per cent of the mass, the hydrogen to helium reactions can go on for a long time, resulting in the long, steady, adult stage of the star's existence.

THE MASS-LUMINOSITY RELATION

If the absolute magnitude and temperature of a main sequence star are to remain essentially constant for millions of years, the energy produced in the nuclear core must be equal to the energy radiated from the star's photosphere. A very massive star would be able to maintain a large core under high enough temperature and pressure conditions to produce nuclear energy at a very rapid rate, giving the star a very bright absolute magnitude. A star of little mass could maintain only a small nuclear core, producing relatively little energy, and thus the star would be faint. By plotting the absolute magnitudes of a large number of main sequence stars against their masses the mass-luminosity relation can be clearly demonstrated.

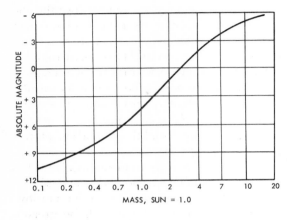

Figure 10.2. The absolute magnitude of a main sequence star depends on its total mass.

STELLAR EVOLUTION

Stars must originate as huge, cool, low-density clouds which contract, compress their gases so they become hot and eventually begin to shine. Rather quickly on a cosmic time scale the central core will have attained high enough temperature and pressure to produce nuclear energy and the star will have moved from the right onto the main sequence of the Russell-Hertzsprung diagram (Figure 9.5). If the star is several times as massive as the sun it may have hundreds of times the sun's luminosity and will become a blue giant, using up its nuclear fuel so extravagantly that its main sequence lifetime may be only a few tens of millions of years. If the star's mass is only a fraction of the sun's it may never attain more than a thousandth or less of the sun's luminosity, but it may remain on the main sequence for hundreds of billions of years as a red dwarf.

A star probably ends its main sequence life when about an eighth of its hydrogen has been converted to helium. With the bulk of the depletion occurring in the core, not enough energy could be produced there to balance the gravitational forces and the central regions would contract, producing higher temperatures and pressures and permitting nuclear reactions between heavier atoms. For example, in a series of reactions, three helium nuclei may combine to form a carbon nucleus.

The core of a star similar to the sun may reach a temperature of 100,000,000°K. Surrounding the central core there would be a shell in which the temperatures, pressures and available hydrogen would be appropriate for the continuation of the hydrogen to helium reactions. Thus the total energy production is increased so the star will gradually brighten by several magnitudes after it leaves the main sequence.

Though the central regions of the star may be contracting, the increasing opacity of the outer regions causes the outer shells of the star to expand at this stage. If the diamater of the star increased to one hundred times its former value, its surface would have increased by one million times, and even though its total radiation might be increased by a factor of 100, the amount of radiation per square foot of its surface would be reduced to only 1/10,000 its main sequence value. The star's photosphere would thus be relatively cool and would appear red, giving us the red giants which appear in the upper righthand portion of the Russell-Hertzsprung diagram.

There must eventually come a time when the elements available for nuclear production of energy in a star of moderate mass become depleted to the point where the star can no longer maintain its former outflow of energy. When this happens, the gravitational forces will be greater than the combined gas and radiation pressures and the star will start to contract. The star will not have transformed more than a few per cent of its mass into energy, so the gravitational contraction will produce some energy, but the star will shrink and become much fainter. Because what energy it is giving off must be radiated from such a small surface the photosphere will become hotter, resulting in a very faint yellow or white dwarf star. On the Russell-Hertzsprung diagram the star probably moves first to the left from the red giant position and then downward to a position below the main sequence. These white dwarfs are said to have the mass of a star and the size of a large planet. Their average density may exceed fifty thousand times the density of water.

MASSIVE STARS

If the mass of a star exceeds about 1.4 times the sun's mass the early stages of its evolution are probably similar to those just described, but it can go farther. Because of its great mass it can maintain its central core at very high temperatures, and as one set of nuclear reactions become exhausted in the core they move out into a shell and the central regions become hotter and more dense, providing the conditions needed for reactions between still heavier elements. The most massive stars may attain a central temperature of 6 billion degrees with up to seven concentric shells, each transforming matter into energy by a different set of nuclear reactions. The resulting red supergiants may be ten thousand times as bright as our sun and have a diameter in excess of 400,000,000 miles.

Though we cannot actually observe the interiors of the stars, the descriptions just given are not the result of wild guessing. The astrophysicist pictures a star as being made up of a large number of concentric shells, like the layers in an onion. The total material in all the shells must add up to the known total mass of the star. The gravitational forces tending to contract each shell must be exactly balanced by the gas pressure and radiation pressure trying to expand it. The temperatures and pressures in the central regions must be exactly right to produce the amount of nuclear energy which is being radiated by the star. The temperature and pressure gradients at each level within the star must be precisely those needed to cause the exact amount of energy produced at the core to be transmitted uniformly out to the photosphere. If any one of these conditions were not satisfied, the diameter, luminosity or temperature of the star would change suddenly.

SUPERNOVAE

There is good evidence that when an extremely massive star tries to move to temperatures above 6 billion degrees the nuclear reactions are of a different nature, becoming endothermic rather than exothermic, that is, absorbing energy instead of giving it off. This would cool the core of the star and cause it to collapse suddenly. The surrounding shells, deprived of their internal support, would be drawn in and compressed, and the resulting increase in both temperature and pressure would cause each of them to speed up its energy production almost explosively. For a few hours or days, until the star is blown to pieces, the energy production and radiation from the star would be accelerated to the point at which it would be radiating more than a hundred million times as rapidly as our sun, giving it an absolute magnitude of about −16. When a star is observed to brighten suddenly and tremendously in this way it is called a supernova. There are three recorded cases of supernovae in our Milky Way Galaxy in the past thousand years, and many have been observed in other galaxies. In each instance, the star increased hundreds of millions of times in brightness within a few days and then faded away more slowly, ejecting material in all directions at speeds which have been measured as high as 3000 miles a second.

We have seen that stars comparable in mass to our sun, after passing the red giant stage, contract smoothly into white dwarfs. Extremely massive stars seem to blow themselves up as supernovae, but what becomes of the stars whose masses are only a few times as great as that of the sun? The answer to this question is not entirely clear, but some interesting evidence is accumulating.

Theoretical investigations lead us to believe that no star having a mass greater than 1.2 solar masses could be a white dwarf, and the masses of the few white dwarfs that have been measured are in complete agreement with the theory. Yet, it is the more massive stars that should evolve most rapidly, and thus the white dwarfs which we can see must be the remnants of stars which were originally several times as massive as the sun. Investigations now going on seem to indicate several different ways in which stars are apparently losing mass.

NOVAE

From time to time, novae (not to be confused with supernovae) are observed in our own and other galaxies. These are stars which, within a few days or less, increase by thousands or even tens of thousands of times in brightness, and then dim slowly over years or tens of years to nearly their original luminosity. They seem to be subdwarfs both before and after the outburst, indicating that the activity is probably associated primarily with the outer layers of the star rather than with its central core. During the sudden rise to maximum brightness and for sometime thereafter, the spectroscope shows that the outer layers of the star are expanding at speeds that sometimes exceed 600 miles per second, more than a thousand times the velocity of a bullet fired from a high-powered rifle. No typical nova has ever been observed to flare up more than once, but reliable observations go back only a few thousand years. If the outbursts came at intervals on the order of ten thousand years we would have no record of any previous activity. When the prenova star is plotted on the H–R diagram, its position seems to fall close to the path predicted for the stars that are shrinking from red giants to white dwarfs. Much of the evidence, both theoretical and observational, points to the possibility that in the shrinking process the more massive stars become unstable and erupt as novae, blowing away some of their material in successive outbursts until their mass has been reduced enough that they can become relatively stable white dwarfs.

PULSATING VARIABLES

Although most stars remain very constant in magnitude over long periods of time, there is one group, the pulsating variables, which display a rhythmic change in brightness that may amount to several magnitudes. Spectroscopic observations show that at least the outer layers of these stars are alternately contracting and expanding with the same period as the light variation and that their spectral class changes along with the pulsation. The RR Lyrae stars have periods from one and one-half to twenty-four hours, change in brightness by about one magnitude and are of spectral class A and F. The Cepheid variables have periods of from one to forty-five days, change their brightness by a little more than a magnitude and are of spectral class F and G. The RV Tauri stars of spectral class G and K have a double pulsation period, one of something less than one hundred days, with alternate minima frequently differing quite sharply, which is superimposed on a much longer variation lasting for a few years. The total range in brightness is two magnitudes or more. The long period variables are mostly red giants of spectral class M, with a somewhat irregular period ranging between one hundred and one thousand days. Though the change in their total radiation probably amounts to something like one and one-half magnitudes, their apparent luminosity may change by more than a thousand times. This is because when they are coolest most of their light is too red to be seen by the human eye, but when they become hotter their radiation moves into the visible range.

There is as yet no completely satisfactory explanation of why the pulsating variables act the way they do. The location of these stars on the H–R diagram strongly suggests that they might be former giant stars that are in the earlier periods of their contraction toward the white dwarf stage. Certainly, they are not operating under the stable conditions of the main sequence stars. One is tempted to assume that these are stars with too much mass to contract smoothly toward a white dwarf stage and that their instability results from an excess of material, but more information, both observational and theoretical, is needed before such a statement can be made with confidence.

The Cepheid variables, divided into two groups, the Type I, or Classical Cepheids, and the Type II Cepheids, or W Virginis stars, have provided the astronomer with an extremely powerful tool. Within each group it has been found that the period of the light variation is directly related to the absolute magnitude, or intrinsic luminosity of the star. Thus, when the period of a Cepheid has been determined we can find its absolute magnitude directly from the period-luminosity curve. The apparent magnitude is obtained directly by observation, and the comparison of the apparent and absolute magnitudes gives the star's distance. Since the Cepheids are giant stars with luminosities ranging from one hundred to ten thousand times the luminosity of the sun, they can be observed even though they may be very far away. They have even enabled us to measure the distances to some of the nearer galaxies that are up to several million light years from our own Milky Way Galaxy.

POPULATION TYPES

When the absolute magnitudes and spectral classes of a significant number of stars had been determined and were plotted on the H—R diagram, it was quite evident that a large majority were located close to a line we now call the main sequence. The bright stars were hot and blue, the blue giants; the faint ones, cool and red, the red dwarfs. The sun was located near the middle of this sequence. A few stars were bright and red, the red giants and supergiants, and a few were blue or yellow and very faint, the so-called white dwarfs. Most of these stars were comparatively near the sun and were thus located in the spiral arms of our galaxy, where nebulous clouds of gas and dust are common. Most of the stars, particularly those on the main sequence, are probably relatively young stars. Stars showing these characteristics are now frequently referred to as a Type I population (Figure 9.5).

As telescopes became more powerful and the necessary information became available for more distant stars, it became apparent that the stars located in globular clusters, in the centers of spirals and in the elliptical galaxies display a strikingly different pattern when plotted on the H—R diagram. Blue giants were almost nonexistent, red giants and supergiants were common, and the main sequence was not to be found but was replaced by a two-branched pattern, with the two branches joining in the region of the red giants (Figure 10.3). Groups of stars displaying these characteristics are said to constitute a Type II population. The high correlation between the distribution of the Type II stars and the evolutionary tracks theoretically developed for aging stars leads us to conclude that the Type II stars constitute an old population. It has been observed repeatedly that interstellar clouds of gas and dust from which young stars form are commonly found associated with Type I stars but are not found in the Type II population regions. The fact that both Type I and Type II populations seem to coincide in the regions of the red dwarfs is not surprising. These unmassive stars evolve so slowly that they have not yet started to move away from the main sequence.

The possibility that Type I and Type II stars represent young and old populations, respectively, suggests that a search be made for groups of stars of intermediate age. There are many galactic star clusters containing from a few score to several hundred stars each, and it is a reasonable assumption that all the individuals in a particular cluster may be about the same chronological age. The more massive and therefore brighter stars in any cluster would be expected to be farther along in their evolutionary sequence than the less massive stars. For a very young cluster only the most massive stars would have started to evolve away from the main sequence, producing only a slight hook in the upper part

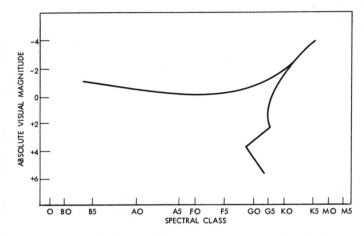

Figure 10.3. The Russell-Hertzsprung spectrum-luminosity diagram for Type II population stars.

of the curve. Somewhat older clusters should display a more pronounced hook, and very old clusters should display almost a Type II population distribution. The H–R diagrams for the three clusters shown in Figure 10.4 demonstrate that the confirmation provided in this way is very satisfactory.

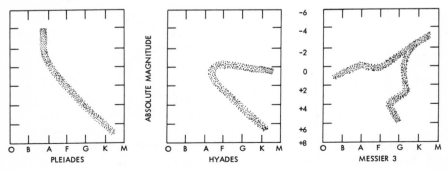

Figure 10.4. Russell-Hertzsprung curves for three star clusters, believed to indicate various ages for their respective stellar populations.

SUMMARY

To the naked-eye observer the stars appear merely as pinpoints of light, some brighter, others very faint, holding fixed positions in the sky year after year and century after century. In contrast to this, our present knowledge of stars presents a rather imposing total. We can determine the distance to a star and its motion through space. We can find its luminosity, its temperature, its mass and its chemical composition. We can describe its rotation and measure the strength of its magnetic field. We can give a reasonably satisfactory picture of the conditions in its interior, explain how it produces the energy it radiates, describe its past history and predict its future life and death. There are, of course, many questions for which the answers are not clear, countless opportunities for further research, but considering the difficulties and complexities of the problems, it is not surprising that questions still remain unanswered. The real marvel is that we have been able to learn so much.

CHAPTER

11

Galaxies

TOPICS

THE MILKY WAY GALAXY

Anyone who looks at the sky on a clear, moonless summer evening will notice that the brighter stars seem to be randomly but relatively evenly distributed over the entire heavens. The very faint stars, however, show a marked concentration toward a rather broad band of diffuse light, the Milky Way, which crosses the sky from the northeast to the southwest during July and August. This would suggest that the stars are not just scattered willy-nilly throughout all space but that there is some form and organization to their distribution.

Nearly two centuries ago, Sir William Herschel suggested that the shape of our galaxy of stars resembled that of a grindstone, a thin, flat disk. From our modern visual and radio telescope observations we know that there is a rounded central condensation about 10,000 l.y. thick, from which spiral arms wind outward to form a flattened disc that is close to 100,000 l.y. in diameter. The nucleus is composed largely of Type II stars and the spiral arms contain mostly Type I stars together with vast

Figure 11.1. A star cloud in the Milky Way in the constellation Sagittarius photographed with the 48-inch Schmidt telescope at the Palomar Observatory. Photograph from the Mount Wilson and Palomar Observatories.

clouds of gas and dust. The whole system is in a slow rotation, with the central regions turning more rapidly than the outer parts. Thus, the spiral arms are gradually becoming wrapped more tightly around the nucleus. Surrounding this flattened system is an almost spherical volume which contains a sparse population of Type II stars. In the other parts of this spherical substratum we know about one hundred globular star clusters, each containing from fifty thousand to several hundred thousand Type II stars. The entire galaxy is believed to contain approximately one hundred billion stars and to have a mass approximately one hundred billion times the mass of the sun.

Our sun, and therefore the earth, is located about 30,000 l.y. from the center of the galaxy, slightly to the north of the central plane and toward the inner edge of one of the spiral arms. From this position many of the stars in the central web are so distant they cannot be seen individually, but the combined light of billions of them produces the band of illumination which we know as the Milky Way. It completely encircles the sky and is inclined at an angle of 62 degrees to the plane of the earth's equator. The portion of the Milky Way which we see in the summer is much brighter than the part we see in the winter, reaching a maximum in the constellation of Sagittarius. This is the direction toward the galactic center, visible just above the southern horizon during the early evenings of July and August.

GALACTIC ROTATION

If the center of our galaxy rotates more rapidly than the outer portions, stars closer to the center than we are must be overtaking and passing us, and we must be overtaking and passing stars that are outside our position. By combining the spectroscopic Doppler shifts of a number of stars in each portion of the Milky Way so their individual space velocities average out, the resulting mean radial velocities are found to be exactly what would be expected if the velocity of rotation became less with increasing distance from the galactic center.

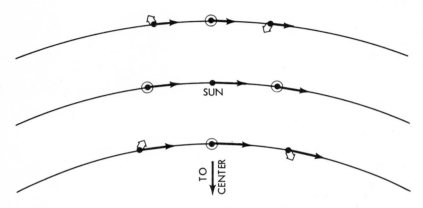

Figure 11.2. Open arrows show velocities with respect to the sun which result from the rotation of the galaxy.

By observing the Doppler shifts in the spectra of other galaxies completely outside our Milky Way we learn that the sun is orbiting the center of our galaxy at a speed of 150 to 200 miles per second. Since we are about 30,000 l.y. from the glactic center, the sun must take something like two hundred million years to complete one orbit. The age of our galaxy is probably less than ten billion years, so the sun must have completed less than fifty complete revolutions since our galaxy was formed.

GALACTIC NEBULAE

Throughout the spiral arms of the Milky Way Galaxy, most of the interstellar spaces seem to be permeated with an extremely rarified cloud of gas and dust. In some regions, this nebulous material is of such low density that it is practically undetectable. In other regions, the density is high enough that the diffuse nebulosity is easily observable, but even the most concentrated parts contain, on the average, much less material per cubic centimeter than the best vacuum that can be attained in our laboratories.

The appearance of these galactic nebulae depends on the presence or absence of nearby stars. If there are no stars reasonably close to a particular cloud of nebulous material, we get no light from it and its presence is detected only by the way the light from more distant stars is made fainter and redder as it passes through the cloud. If the nebula contains stars that are cooler than about 18,000°K, their light is simply reflected by the material in the nebula and its spectrum is the same as that of the stars which are producing the light. If the stars are hotter than 18,000°K, their light will be very strong in the extremely short wave lengths, ultraviolet and soft X-rays. This high-energy radiation is absorbed by the nebulous material and reradiated in the visible light region in the form of a bright-line spectrum. Thus, clouds of essentially identical composition may appear as dark nebulae, reflection nebulae or emission nebulae, depending on the nearness and nature of the associated stars.

PLANETARY NEBULAE

Early observers with visual telescopes noted a considerable number of small objects which were clearly not ordinary stars. Because, like the planets, they showed a small disc, they were called planetary nebulae even though they are in no way associated with the planets. Larger telescopes and astronomical photography show that some of them have the appearance of a complete or broken smoke ring. Others are brighter near the center and fade away farther out, often breaking up into a filamented structure. Many of them appear to have a small but hot star near their centers, and all have a bright-line spectrum. In a few cases, a slow expansion of the nebula has been measured. It now seems clearly established that at least some of the planetary nebulae are simply the expanding cloud of gas produced by the explosion of a supernova.

GALACTIC STAR CLUSTERS

Within our galaxy, we recognize several hundred star clusters which contain from a few to many hundred stars. These are not just chance groupings. Identical space velocities of all its members indicate that each cluster should be considered a separate entity. The reasonable assumption that all the individuals in a given cluster were formed at about the same time would give them all the same chronological age, and thus differences in their luminosity, spectrum and other characteristics probably resulted from differences in their original mass and its effect on their rates of evolution. Studies of the galactic star clusters have thus

Figure 11.3. The Orion Nebula is one of the more spectacular galactic nebulae. Photograph from the Mount Wilson and Palomar Observatories.

Figure 11.4. The crab Nebula in Taurus resulted from the outburst of a supernova observed in A.D. 1054. Photograph from the Mount Wilson Palomar Observatories.

Figure 11.5. One of the best known of the galactic star clusters is this double cluster in Perseus. Lick Observatory photograph.

Figure 11.6. The globular star cluster M3 in Canes Venatici. Lick Observatory photograph.

provided significant information dealing with the manner in which individual stars develop.

Though the distances between the individual stars in a cluster is appreciably less than the average distance between stars in the galaxy, their spacing should not be thought of as even remotely approaching the scale of planetary separation. Five of the seven stars in the Big Dipper, some of the stars in Orion and other stars in various directions from the sun all show identical space velocities and are therefore members of the same cluster. It is currently passing through the part of the galaxy in which our sun is located. We are thus within a cluster but are not a member of it.

GLOBULAR CLUSTERS

The globular clusters which are located in the outer parts of the nearly spherical substratum that surrounds the Milky Way Galaxy are quite different in constitution from the galactic clusters. They contain from fifty thousand to several hundred thousand stars each, and average perhaps a hundred l.y. in diameter. The stars seem to be most strongly concentrated toward the center of the cluster where the population density may be in excess of one hundred stars per cubic parsec. Normal stellar populations in the arms of the galaxy would have only one star for several cubic parsecs.

The stars in the globular clusters seem to be exclusively of Type II population, which would imply that they are far along in their evolutionary sequence. No evidence of interstellar clouds of gas or dust has been found. Thus far, no really satisfactory explanation of their origin has been proposed.

OTHER GALAXIES

For the first three centuries after the invention of the telescope, astronomers believed that the many small, hazy objects they observed were merely nebulous stars or compact clouds of nebulous material. Early in the present century, Harlow Shapley was able to show that they were not small objects located within our Milky Way Galaxy but were complete galaxies in themselves, comparable in every way to our own, and were at distances ranging from a few million to (as we now know) several billion light years. The total number of these galaxies is unknown, but there are perhaps ten billion of them within the reach of our present telescopes.

Though we can observe vast numbers of individual systems, they all fall into one of three major classifications: spirals, elliptical galaxies and irregular galaxies. The spirals are subdivided into normal spirals and barred spirals. There is a rather wide range in size, brightness and

Figure 11.7. Three normal spirals and one barred spiral. Photographs from the Mount Wilson and Palomar Observatories.

other characteristics among the galaxies of any particular class, but if we examine a reasonable number of each type in some detail we can feel confident that we understand at least the major characteristics of all similar systems.

The spirals constitute the most spectacular group of galaxies. Normal spirals consist of a more or less spherical central nucleus from which there extends a relatively thin flat web in which spiral arms are prominent. Our own Milky Way system is of this type. Surrounding both the nucleus and the spiral arms is a more nearly spherical region, the substratum, in which the density of the stellar population is much lower than in either the nucleus or the spiral arms. The nucleus contains a large fraction of the mass of the entire galaxy and is composed of Type II stars that are well along in their evolutionary process. Little, if any, interstellar gas and dust is found in the nucleus. The spiral arms, however, are composed largely of Type I population stars that are in the relatively early stages of their development. Perhaps 20 per cent of the mass of the arms is made of nebulous clouds of gas and dust. Since stars are believed to develop from just such material, the association of young stars and clouds of gas and dust is not surprising. The surrounding substratum is populated with Type II stars, and though its boundaries are not clearly defined, it contributes a sizable fraction of the total light coming from a spiral. Rather sophisticated techniques must be employed to learn the characteristics of these tremendously distant galaxies. Velocities of 100 miles a second in their various parts would produce a scarcely detectable change in their appearance in 1 million years. In all but a few of the very nearest, even the brightest of the normal stars would be too faint to be seen or photographed with our most powerful telescopes. However, supernovae attain a maximum absolute magnitude of about −16, and they have been observed in distant galaxies. Knowing the actual luminosity of the supernova and how bright it appears to us, we can calculate its distance. With the distance to a galaxy known and its angular dimensions taken from photographs, we can calculate its linear dimensions. When a rotating galaxy is almost edgewise to our line of sight, the Doppler shifts in its spectrum show the velocities with which its various parts are approaching or receding from our instruments. We can thus determine its period of rotation at different distances from the center. Once the period is known for a given distance from the center, the mass which would be required to maintain that rotation can be computed.

We have seen that our own Milky Way Galaxy is a normal spiral which is between 80,000 and 100,000 l.y. in diameter and 8,000 to 10,000 l.y. in thickness. The Great Spiral in Andromeda is probably a bit larger, and both are among the largest spirals known. In general, spirals have diameters between 10,000 and 100,000 l.y. and masses from ten billion to two hundred billion times the mass of the sun. None of the spirals have nuclei whose thickness is more than 3/10 the diameter of the arms. As would be suspected from their shape, the spirals are all rotating with speeds which increase toward the center. Thus, the nucleus is winding itself up in the spiral arms. Spirals are sometimes further classified with respect to whether the spiral arms are noticeably more prominent, about equally prominent or noticeably less prominent than the nucleus.

Between 1/3 and 1/4 of all spirals have their arms originating from the ends of a straight bar, rather than winding outward directly from the central nucleus. In these Barred Spirals, the structure of the straight portion is similar to that of the spiral arms, but there is as yet no clear explanation of why some spirals have one form and some another.

The elliptical galaxies constitute the second group. In some ways, they are like spiral galaxies without the spiral arms and dust clouds, but they are uniformly thicker than spirals. Some are almost spherical, and the thinnest have a central thickness about 3/10 their diameter. They show no internal structure and are composed exclusively of a Type II stellar population. In size they range from larger than the largest spirals to smaller than the smallest. Although the majority of the bright, conspicuous galaxies in the sky are spirals, in any given volume of space there are probably more elliptical systems, many of them relatively faint.

Figure 11.8 An elongated elliptical galaxy in Cassiopeia and a globular elliptical galaxy in Virgo. Photographs from the Mount Wilson and Palomar Observatories.

Irregular galaxies constitute the third group. They are systems that show no rotational symmetry but, as their name implies, are irregularly shaped and apparently without internal organization. Most of them seem to contain both Type I and Type II stars, together with clouds of gas and dust. A few seem to have little or no dust, and some have not as yet been resolved into stars. Numberwise, they probably constitute the smallest of the three groups of galaxies, but because many of them are relatively faint, an accurate estimate of their number is difficult. The two nearest and brightest extragalactic systems in our sky, the Large and Small Magellanic Clouds, are usually considered to be irregular galaxies, though the Large Cloud is slightly suggestive of a barred spiral.

As a rough approximation to the distribution of the galaxies, we may assume they are located at random, with an average distance of perhaps 2 million light years between any individual and its nearest

Figure 11.9. The Magellanic clouds. Yerkes Observatory photograph.

neighbor. Superimposed on this random distribution, however, we must recognize the tendency of galaxies to occur in clusters of anywhere from two or three to several thousand individuals. Within a cluster the intergalactic spacing would be appreciably less than the average distance given above. There is even a possibility, according to some recent investigations, that most of the galaxies which we can see are members of a supergalactic system which is slowly revolving around its own center of gravity.

GALACTIC EVOLUTION

The possibility that the various types of galaxies may constitute different stages in some form of an evolutionary sequence is worth

Figure 11.10. Part of a cluster of galaxies in Coma Berenices at a distance of about 40 million light years from the earth photographed with the 200-inch Hale Telescope. Photograph from the Mount Wilson and Palomar Observatories.

considering. It must be noted that (1) irregular galaxies have no symmetry, have appreciable amounts of gas and dust and many Type I young stars, (2) spirals have more symmetry, young Type I stars together with gas and dust in the arms and old Type II stars without gas and dust in their central nuclei and surrounding envelope and (3) elliptical systems seem to be almost exclusively old Type II stars with no dust and probably little or no gas. It would seem that any evolutionary process would have to move from irregulars to spirals to elliptical galaxies. However, it is difficult to see how a highly flattened spiral could evolve into an almost spherical elliptical galaxy. Many astronomers now suspect that there is little evolution between galaxies of different types and that the form of a galaxy is determined very early by the characteristics of the original cloud from which the galaxy developed.

THE RED-SHIFT DISTANCE RELATIONSHIP

When the world's largest telescopes were first used to obtain the spectra of galaxies over a wide range of distances from the earth, an unexpected and surprising discovery was made. Not only are the lines in all their spectra (except for a few of the very nearest) shifted to the red, but the amount of the red shift is directly proportional to the distance of the galaxy. The great difficulty of determining reliable distances for galaxies located hundreds of millions or even billions of light years from the earth leaves some uncertainty as to the precise numerical values that should be assigned, but it now seems clear that the wavelength of a spectral line is increased by about 1/10,000 its normal wavelength for each million light years of the galaxy's distance from the earth. There can be no question about the validity of the observations. The lines in the spectra of each galaxy are shifted to the red by an amount which is closely proportional to the galaxy's distance from the earth.

The cause of the red-shift distance relationship is, however, still uncertain. One obvious explanation is that these red shifts are really Doppler shifts and that all the observed galaxies are receding from the earth at speeds which are directly proportional to their distances. If this is the correct explanation, and most astronomers today feel it is the most likely of several theories that have been advanced, then we can say that each of the galaxies is receding from us at a speed of about 20 miles per second for each million light years of its distance. The red shifts in some of the faintest galaxies indicate velocities of recession close to 90,000 miles per second, half the velocity of light. This would indicate a distance from the sun in excess of four billion light years.

One of the alternate theories that has been suggested is that light simply gets tired traveling over such vast distances. We know that the energy contained in a quantum of light is directly proportional to the frequency of the light or inversely proportional to its wavelength. Simply stated, blue light has more energy per quantum than red. Suppose that in the mere process of traveling across the tremendous distances of intergalactic space a train of light waves used up some of its original energy. It would seem reasonable to expect that this loss of energy would be apparent as a reddening of the light, that is, as an increase in the wavelength. It would also seem reasonable to expect that the amount of reddening would be proportional to the distance the light had traversed. The physicists, however, feel quite confident that they have a good understanding of how light waves are propagated, and they have been unable to come up with any explanation of how light might gradually lose energy as it travels through space. Until they do, and it is quite possible that no such explanation exists, the tired-light theory cannot be accepted.

Another suggested explanation involves the possibility that some sort of a physical change might be taking place in the material of the universe over long periods of time. When we photograph the Great Spiral in Andromeda, at a distance of nearly 2 million light years, we photograph it not as it is today, but as it was nearly two million years ago when the light we are now seeing left the spiral. Galaxies in the Ursa Major cluster are at a distance of 170,000,000 light years, so we are seeing them as they were one hundred seventy million years ago. The most distant systems known are at distances of the order of 6 billion light years, so we must be seeing them as they were six billion years ago. It thus becomes apparent that as we look out through space we are unavoidably looking back through time. If there is some physical change that is going on slowly throughout the universe, if, for example, all atoms radiated longer wavelengths a billion years ago than they do today, then as we look out to more and more distant objects, we would be observing them as they were farther and farther back in time. But, like the tired-light theory, no one has been able to give any reasonable explanation of how or why this kind of a change might have occurred, and the physical change theory has had few supporters.

Other proposals have been made. Some coming from relativity, for example, suggest that the red shift may in some way be associated with the curvature of space, or perhaps, with a changing radius of the curvature of space in different parts of the universe. Though all these theories have been carefully considered, none seem to be as acceptable as the original assumption that the red shifts are actually Doppler shifts and that the galaxies are receding from our location with speeds that are directly proportional to their distances.

THE EXPANDING UNIVERSE

It may seem at first that if everything is moving away from our position we must be at the center, but this does not follow. Actually, if this were a necessary conclusion it would constitute a strong argument against the theory. Why, out of billions of galaxies should our Milky Way be the center? The odds are billions to one against it, and any theory which makes the observer's position unique is to be regarded with distrust. A simple illustration may make the true situation more apparent.

Suppose we had an elastic chessboard with twenty or thirty pieces located on it at random, each piece standing at the center of one of the squares. Let us, also, take a position at the center of one of the squares, preferably not in one of the outside rows. We will make note of the direction and distance of each of the other pieces from our location. Now suppose we stretch the board in every direction to twice its original size. The various pieces on the board will remain the same size and will continue to occupy the centers of their original squares, but as the board is stretched they will all move farther apart. The pieces which are close to us will seem to be moving away from our position relatively slowly; the more distant pieces will be moving away at higher speeds. As a matter of fact, each piece will be moving away from us with a speed that is directly proportional to its distance. Since no specific square was designated for our position we could have occupied any vacant square and the experiment would have had precisely the same result. Translating this demonstration back to the expanding universe it should be evident that as long as there is a uniform expansion, the distance between any pair of galaxies that might be selected will be increasing and the rate of increase will be proportional to the distance between them. Thus, regardless of where we may be located in an expanding universe, all the other galaxies will be receding from us with a speed that is proportional to their distance, 20 miles per second for each million light years.

QUASISTELLAR SOURCES

Within the last several years a new type of object, the quasistellar source, or quasar has been discovered. Perhaps they should be considered to be a fourth class of galaxies, but not enough is yet known to justify this classification.

The objects were first detected by radio telescopes and then observed by optical instruments. They are relatively bright and can be seen as a starlike object in a comparatively small instrument. Their spectra are unlike the spectra of normal stars, and it was some time before it was recognized that what was being observed was the normally invisible ultraviolet spectrum of a star which had been red-shifted down into the visual region. If we assume that the same red-shift distance relation that is used with galaxies can be applied to quasars, they are found to be extremely distant, up to 8 billion light years in fact, and would thus be the most distant objects ever observed. To look as bright as they do at this tremendous distance they would have to be hundreds of times as bright as the brightest galaxies. No physical process is known which would explain such extreme luminosity.

Both the tremendous distances and the incomprehensible brightness ascribed to the quasars depend on the unverified assumption that they fit the same red shift-distance relation that is used for galaxies. Changes in brightness and very recently, changes in their apparent size have been observed which would seem to be completely impossible if their distances are actually billions of light years. Hopefully, research now in progress may lead to a satisfactory explanation of these intriguing objects.

THE ORIGIN OF THE UNIVERSE

The mass of the sun has already been stated as about 2000 million million million million tons, and it is only one of perhaps one hundred billion stars in our galaxy. There are probably ten billion galaxies within the reach of our present telescopes, and we can only guess as to how many more there may be which we are unable to observe. What this all adds up to is an incomprehensibly vast amount of material currently in existance.

No one can say how the protons, neutrons and electrons that make up this tremendous mass came into existence. Perhaps they have always been here, in one form or another, but this runs into an infinite time scale which defies comprehension. Perhaps they were formed from some earlier material or from pure energy, but we would then ask where the earlier material or the pure energy came from. There seems to be no scientific explanation of how matter originally came into being. We can only accept its existence and try to see how it was transformed and molded into the present form of the universe.

If we accept the red shifts in the spectra of the galaxies as Doppler shifts we are, in effect, accepting the idea that the universe is expanding. There is no evidence that the individual galaxies are getting larger. It is only the distances between them that is increasing, presumably at a steady rate. Three interpretations seem possible. Perhaps the expansion is the result of some kind of a catastrophic explosion which blew everything apart. This is popularly called the "Big Bang" theory. Perhaps the universe has always been expanding at the present rate, a proposal that is known as the "Steady State," or uniformitarian theory. Perhaps the universe alternately expands and contracts, with periods of many billions of years between successive contractions and expansions. This could be called the "pulsating universe." Let us look briefly at each of these three proposals.

The Big Bang Theory

Though the red shift in the spectrum of a galaxy can be measured very acurately, the distance to the galaxy is more difficult to determine precisely. Thus, the Hubble constant, or the rate of expansion of the universe, is somewhat uncertain, but the value is probably close to 20 miles per second for each million light years that a galaxy is distant from the earth.

If we assume that at one time the galaxies were very close together and that the rate of expansion has been constant, we need only divide the distance of 1 million light years (5.87×10^{18} miles) by the speed of 20 miles per second to find the time interval since the expansion began. It turns out to be about 300,000 million million seconds, or ten billion years. Recognizing the uncertainties in some of the figures, it is better not to attempt to be too exact, but to say that the expansion of the galaxies probably began between ten and fifteen billion years ago.

It is postulated that at that time all the material now in the universe was assembled into one huge cosmic atom composed of a vast jumble of individual protons, neutrons and electrons. Temperatures, densities and pressures millions of times higher than anything we can even imagine would have prevented the formation of atoms as we know them. There is little point in wondering about the structure of the universe prior to this time, since any forms that existed before the cosmic atom state would have been completely destroyed and the material broken down into the primordial particles.

Then came the "big bang," and in one indescribably violent explosion the cosmic atom was torn to pieces and the material thrown out in all directions. The speeds of ejection must have varied widely, with some fragments having velocities close to the speed of light. The sudden cooling which resulted from the rapid expansion would have favored the combination of the protons, neutrons and electrons into atoms and the laws of probability would favor the formation of the lighter elements. Probably more than 85 per cent of the atoms produced were hydrogen, less than 15 per cent were helium, and all the rest of the heavier elements together would constitute less than one per cent. Before the expansion had gone too far, turbulence and gravitational attraction would have caused the gases to collect into billions of more or less separate clouds, each containing from a few billion to a few hundred billion times as much material as our sun. The velocities resulting from the explosion would cause these clouds to become more and more widely separated from each other. Within each individual cloud the gravitational contraction, internal turbulence, friction and the conservation of angular momentum would, in many cases, result in rotational symmetry. The contraction would increase the densities of the gases and the formation of many smaller knots of material within each cloud would be expected. This process might be repeated a number of times, with many smaller condensations forming within each larger one, until at last the chunks are small enough to develop into individual stars. Thus, the big bang theory seems to account reasonably well for the formation of the elements, the expanding universe, the vast numbers of galaxies and the birth of countless billions of stars.

Many astronomers, however, feel that the beginning and ending of a "big bang" universe are something less than satisfactory. At the beginning there is no real explanation of where the material came from, and the very nature of the theory precludes the possibility of consideration of conditions before the time of the cosmic atom. At the other end of the time scale, the "big bang" universe seems capable of nothing but simply running down. In perhaps a few hundred billion years, each galaxy would be far removed from any other, all available material would have been formed into stars, and the stars themselves would have burned out. Many astronomers feel uncomfortable with a theory which simply starts and stops.

The Steady State Theory

A decade or so ago the steady state, or uniformitarian theory enjoyed the support of a considerable number of leading astronomers. Of late its popularity has decreased, but it still appears in astronomical literature and thinking frequently enough to be well worth consideration here.

As the name implies, the steady state theory suggests that conditions within the universe always have been, and always will be much as they now are. It assumes that there never was a beginning and that there never will be an end to the universe. It is impossible for our minds to comprehend a beginning before which neither time nor matter existed. Our choice here is between two ideas, both incomprehensible.

Those who support the steady state idea recognize that if the total amount of matter in the universe remains constant and the universe continues to expand, the inevitable result is a steady decrease in the average density of matter throughout the universe. This would amount to a change in conditions and would not constitute a steady state; therefore, they postulate that matter is being created spontaneously throughout the universe at precisely the proper rate to offset the effects of the expansion, thus maintaining a constant value for the average density of material throughout the universe.

The very idea that material is being created spontaneously out of nothing is abhorrent to most people, and it must be admitted that no satisfactory explanation of just how this matter is being created has ever been suggested. It is equally true, however, that no satisfactory explanation has ever been advanced to account for the material that was needed to initiate the universe by the big bang theory. We may be willing to accept an idea without explanation if it happened ten billion years ago and be unwilling to accept the same idea without explanation if it is going on today. Yet the problem is really identical. No satisfactory explanation can be offered for either proposal.

With the steady state theory we may assume that though the existing galaxies are becoming farther apart, new material is being constantly added, and that, when enough material has been created, it may pull together gravitationally to form new galaxies from which new stars may develop. A look at the human population of the earth at any particular instant would reveal people of all ages: infants, children, adults and the aged. The steady state theory proposes a similar situation for the astronomical universe. At any particular instant in time there should be all types of astronomical bodies at every possible stage in their evolutionary development.

One may reasonably ask what becomes of all the material that is created over an infinite time scale in the steady state theory. The assumption is that with the continuing expansion of the universe there must always be galaxies far distant from us which are going "over the edge," that is, out of our sphere of knowledge. This explanation may seem quite unsatisfactory, and if it does, it is because, like the problems of the creation of matter and infinite time scales, the very nature of the answer is beyond our comprehension. An illustration may help.

Suppose we carefully leveled a perfectly flat, round plate and then poured an ounce of syrup on the center of the plate. The syrup, at first, would cover only a small area with a moderately thick coating. After a few minutes or hours, it would spread to a much larger area, but the coating would be much thinner. This situation would, perhaps inadequately, represent the "big bang" universe. As an alternative, suppose we arrange a device so that occasional drops of syrup fall regularly on various parts of the plate. Once the experiment gets well started, there will be comparatively uniform coating of syrup over the entire plate. There will be a constant addition of syrup from the scattered drops, but there will be an exactly equal amount flowing over the edge of the plate. Thus, the thickness of the layer of syrup at any designated point on the plate remains constant, and we have an illustration of the steady state universe.

The Pulsating Universe

Several decades ago the idea of a pulsating universe was proposed, though at that time it did not receive general acceptance. Recent developments have produced an awakened interest in this possibility.

Let us start with a situation identical to the sudden expansion of the universe after the "big bang." All the material forming into galaxies will be moving outward from the center at the various speeds imparted to them at the time of the explosion. The outward speeds would remain constant and the expansion would go on for ever if there were no forces acting on the material. But the combined masses of all the various parts of the universe will exert a gravitational force, however slight, which will be directed toward the center of the entire system. This force will tend to slow the outward movement of the individual components, and perhaps, after tens of billions of years, stop the expansion entirely. With the gravitational forces continuing, the galaxies would be drawn back to the center so that what was formerly an expanding universe would now become a contracting universe. The forces acting on the various galaxies would be so slight that the motions would be extremely slow at first, and the time required for the universe to contract back to the center would be just as long as the time during which it was expanding.

In the final stages of the contraction much of the material would be rushing in with speeds approaching the velocity of light, resulting in the compression of all the material in the universe into, again, a great cosmic atom. Here the temperatures and pressures would again be so great that not only would stars and galaxies be unable to maintain their identity, but even the individual atoms would be broken down into their component protons, neutrons and electrons. From this mass of material we would expect another big bang, and the beginning of another cycle of expansion and contraction, complete with the formation of new galaxies, new stars, and, in fact, a repetition of the preceding cycle. Since there would seem to be no limit to the number of times this process could be repeated it is usually referred to as the pulsating universe theory. A. R. Sandage has suggested a period of about eighty-two billion years for one complete pulsation.

CONCLUSION

This, all too briefly, has been the story of *Astronomy and the Origin of the Earth*. It began with the earth and worked outward through the solar system, the stars, the galaxies, and ended with some cosmological theories of the origin of the universe. From an evolutionary standpoint, the order of the chapters should, perhaps, have been reversed.

Our present understanding of astronomy is the result of centuries of careful investigation by dedicated scientists. During the past few decades larger optical telescopes, radio telescopes, satellites and space probes, and powerful computers, manned by an ever-increasing number of highly trained men and women, have resulted in an almost explosive increase in our knowledge. In spite of these gains, that which is known must be but a minute fraction of that which is unknown.

Perhaps this is the great appeal of astronomy, that regardless of how much may be discovered, some place in the depths of space there will be new questions waiting to challenge the best intellects of the age.

Index

(Page numbers in boldface type indicate illustrations.)